THE ORCHID SOCIETY OF THAILAND
Affiliated with The American Orchid Society, Inc.
Department of Plant Science, Horticulture Sect.
Kasetsart University
Mailing: G.P.O. Box 953, Bangkok, THAILAND

BEAUTIFUL
THAI ORCHID SPECIES

AKSORNSAMPAN

Doritis pulcherrima

BEAUTIFUL
THAI ORCHID SPECIES

Haruyuki Kamemoto
Rapee Sagarik

THE ORCHID SOCIETY OF THAILAND

First Edition 1975

Published by The Orchid Society of Thailand
G.P.O. Box 953, Bangkok, Thailand.

Printed by Aksornsampan Press
Bangkok, Thailand.

PREFACE

The increasing popularity of orchid species of Thailand has created a need for a book describing the major species of horticultural value and discussing their ecology, cultural requirements and hybridization performance and potential. . Thailand is blessed with a wealth of orchid species. *The Orchids of Thailand*, by Seidenfaden and Smitinand, enumerates 858 species, many of which can be classified as horticulturally desirable species.

This book is limited to the treatment of "horticultural" species of Thailand and excludes the many charming "botanicals". It is not easy to draw a distinction between horticultural and botanical species, for a number of the small-flowered species are now being cultivated by hobbyists. However, the small-flowered species are not included in this book unless the inflorescence as a whole is attractive, such as *Rhynchostylis retusa*, or the species are members of a predominantly attractive large-flowered genus such as *Calanthe cardioglossa*.

The color reproductions should provide the reader with a simple means of identifying species. Instead of representing so-called "typical" species, as is the general practice of taxonomists, we have sought exceptional or superior forms of each in order to acquaint the hybridizer with the improved forms available within the species. This should enable him to plan his hybridization program wisely ; he might otherwise utilize an inferior form present in his collection.

The taxonomic treatment in this book is based largely on Seidenfaden and Smitinand's *The Orchids of Thailand* and Holttum's *Flora of Malaya, I, Orchids*. The writers are greatly indebted to Mr. Tem Smitinand for his assistance in identifying several live specimens, and to Dr. Eric Holttum for his advice and help in response to several of our inquiries on taxonomic problems. The authors also wish to express their heartfelt gratitude to the Kasetsart-Hawaii University Contract for supporting the research project on the cytogenetics of orchids conducted in the Department of Horticulture, Kasetsart University, from July 1962 to June 1965. Thanks are also due the late Dean Thiem Komkris of the Forestry Faculty of Kasetsart University for arranging several trips to the forests of Thailand, and to Dr. Yoneo Sagawa, Mrs. L. Kay Krakauer, Miss Beatrice Krauss and Mrs. Shirley Dunbar for reading the manuscript. To our wives, Mrs. Kalya Sagarik and Mrs. Ethel Kamemoto, a special note of thanks for their inspiration, encouragement, and assistance, without which this book would not have become a reality Also the efforts of Mr. Suree Bhumibhamon, Mr. Pisit Sukreeyapong, and Mr. Teerapatra Santimetaneedol in assuming charge of most of the technical aspects of publishing this book are gratefully acknowledged.

Bangkok, Thailand.
June, 1975

CONTENTS

INTRODUCTION

Thailand abounds in indigenous orchid species, some of which are already well known to and extensively cultivated by orchidists throughout the world. Within the past decade the increased interest in Thai orchids by the residents of the country, the timely publication of *The Orchids of Thailand*, by Gunnar Seidenfaden and Tem Smitinand, and the development and improvement of highways in what were once remote inaccessible regions, have combined to bring the beautiful orchid species of Thailand into sharp focus. Species of *Ascocentrum*, *Rhynchostylis*, *Doritis* and *Vanda* from Thailand have assumed significant roles in present-day orchid hybridization. Others will be discovered or rediscovered for breeding purposes.

Seidenfaden and Smitinand enumerated 858 species in *The Orchids of Thailand*. With continued exploration and collecting, aided by the development of new roads, a considerable number of species will be added to the list. The above authors state that "Thailand may well prove to possess the most diversified and numerous orchid flora of the world". Not only is the large number of orchid species impressive but also the high percentage of horticulturally desirable species. Such genera as *Paphiopedilum*, *Cymbidium*, *Vanda* and *Dendrobium*, to name a few, are richly represented in Thailand.

Thailand lies between 5 and 21 degrees N latitude in Southeast Asia ; it occupies 200,000 square miles of land area and is about the size of France. It is bounded by Cambodia on the east and southeast, Laos on the east and northeast, Burma on the northwest and west, and Malaysia on the south. It is not surprising, therefore, that most orchid species of Thailand have common natural distribution in one or more of the neighboring countries.

Extending from the high elevation mountains in the north at 21 degrees N latitude, to the tropical zone at 5 degrees N, Thailand is provided with varied ecological conditions which support highly diversified plant populations. Thailand has been divided into seven phytogeographical regions. These regions, with some prominent locations of orchid distribution for each region, are given below :

    I. North--Chiengmai, Doi Saked, Doi Intanond, Mae Sarieng, Tak
   II. Northeast--Loei, Udornthani
  III. East--Ubolratani, Khonkaen
   VI. Central--Nakornnayok, Bangkok Plains
    V. Southeast--Chandhaburi, Siracha
   VI. Southwest--Khanburi, Petchaburi, Prachuab, Ranong
  VII. Peninsula--Surathani, Krabi, Pattani

According to Seidenfaden and Smitinand, the following numbers of species have been found in each of the phytogeographical regions : I--473, II--200, III--175, IV--52, V--216, VI--148 and VII--385. Based on these figures, the greatest concentration of orchid species is in northern Thailand, followed by southern Thailand.

The climate of Thailand is influenced by the monsoon winds. From November to February, during the northeast monsoon, the cold dry air blows in from Mainland China, resulting in a delightfully cool, dry period. The southwest monsoon, from May to November, brings the warm winds from the Indian Ocean, creating an abundance of rainfall throughout the country. The premonsoon season, or "summer," in March and April is the dry, hot season, while the postmonsoon season in October is a short transitional period between the southwest and the northeast monsoons.

Bangkok, the capital of Thailand, is situated at 14 degrees N and about 3 feet above sea level. The temperatures there during the northeast monsoon season may drop to about $50°$ to $55°$ F ; during the hot, dry months in March, April and early May, temperatures may soar to the 90s and, occasionally, $100°$ F. In the peninsular region of Thailand, temperatures are mild throughout the year, usually ranging from $70°$ to $90°$ F, due to the influence of the surrounding body of ocean, while in the north, hail and frost are not uncommon during winter.

Rainfall varies considerably. In the southern part of Thailand, both monsoons bring rains, while in upper Thailand, rainfall is restricted to the season of the southeast monsoon. Although the annual rainfall is moderately high over most of Thailand, dry regions in the interior of northeastern Thailand, as well as in the northern region of the peninsula, are rather arid, averaging less than 20 inches rainfall a year in some areas. On the other hand, the west coast of the southern part and the east coast of the Gulf of Thailand have the heaviest rainfall, averaging as high as 264 inches annually.

During the winter months, the relative humidity is generally low. With the advent of the hot season, air moisture increases, although due to the dry conditions, the afternoon humidity remains low. The mean relative humidity increases to 80 percent during the rainy season, with many days reaching humidities as high as 90 to 95 percent. The humidity drops to about 66 percent in December and January.

A knowledge of the ecology of orchid species contributes to their successful cultivation. Although Thailand lies in the tropics, many species that inhabit mountain areas of northern Thailand cannot be treated as warm temperature orchids. Even during the hot, dry period in March and April, the night temperatures in their natural habitats may drop to $50°$ F. Some orchid species, such as *Rhynchostylis coelestis* and *Doritis pulcherrima*, are widely distributed ; consequently, the treatment of such species under cultivation is dependent upon the location from which they have been collected. Accordingly, the ecology and distribution of species are presented in the text whenever appropriate.

9

The information given for the culture of most of the species discussed is primarily for Thailand conditions. However, orchidists outside of Thailand should be able to adjust their cultural practices by studying the ecology of the species in their native habitats. The chapters at the end of the book, on collecting orchids in several phytogeographical regions, provide additional information on the ecology and distribution of Thailand orchids. This information should be of value to growers elsewhere.

It is impossible to give an up—to—date, accurate assessment of the performance of species as parents in modern—day hybridization, inasmuch as intensive hybridization conducted throughout the world is resulting in continual introductions of new hybrids. However, since species are the basic building blocks of hybrids, their past breeding performance as well as their potentials for future breeding are discussed briefly.

Cytogenetics has assumed great significance in orchid breeding. Terminology, such as diploids (those with 2 sets of chromosomes--2N), triploids (3N), tetraploids (4N), pentaploids (5N), hexaploids (6N) and polyploids (those with more than 2N), is in common usage among orchids breeders. Also, the knowledge of genome (the chromosome set) relationships is often very useful in interspecific and intergeneric hybridization. With wide species crosses, the hybrids are generally infertile due to poor pairing of the parental chromosomes at meiosis. If the chromosome number of such hybrids is doubled, the tetraploids (or amphidiploids) may be expected to be fully fertile, since they will have two sets, or genomes, each of the parental species.

Some variation in chromosome number exists among the orchid species of Thailand. A few species, namely *Vanda denisoniana*, *Aerides odorata* and *Doritis pulcherrima*, have both diploid and tetraploid varieties occurring in the wilds. These diploid and tetraploid varieties differ markedly in their breeding behavior. A tetraploid variety is expected to exhibit a strong influence on the progeny due to the transmission of two sets of chromosomes. In the genus *Paphiopedilum*, *Paph. callosum* and *Paph. barbatum* can be readily distinguished from other species on the basis of chromosome numbers. Accordingly, chromosome numbers are presented whenever they are important in distinguishing species or in discussions of breeding. When chromosome numbers are known for the species of Thailand discussed in this book, they are presented in the Appendix.

AERIDES

The popular *Aerides* genus in the *Vanda* alliance is represented in Thailand by about eight species, all of which are highly attractive and worthy of cultivation. They generally produce long arching sprays with closely spaced, often fragrant, beautiful flowers. Heavily branched plants with numerous flower sprays make attractive decorations and excellent conversation pieces.

Those species occupying relatively low elevation habitats -- *Aer. falcata,* diploid *Aer. odorata* and *Aer. mitrata* -- are easy to cultivate and flower in the lowlands. Those that come from higher elevations will require cool conditions for flowering. These orchids do well in wooden baskets filled with tree fern and coconut fibers and charcoal, alone or in combinations. They also can be grown without the use of any medium. Plants should be provided with good aeration and drainage, watered copiously and fertilized occasionally. Large plants may need staking due to their tendency to droop.

Like many other native orchids, plants of this genus do exceptionally well without much care if attached to tree trunks and branches. The best location on trees is a spot that will receive direct sunlight in the morning or afternoon, and near or above a pond or other body of water

Aerides odorata Laur.

This is a highly variable species, widely distributed from South China, Indochina, Thailand Burma and Malaysia to the Philippines. In Thailand, it occurs in the northern, northeastern, eastern, southwestern and peninsular regions. The plants from the southern areas are quite distinct from those from the north. The stems are slightly twisted, drooping and branching, and often reach 4 to 5 feet in length. The leaves are about 10 inches long and 1 inch wide, unequally bilobed, relatively thin and flexible, slightly twisted and reflexed toward the apical portion. Usually around May, several arching and drooping inflorescences, about 16 inches long, are produced, each bearing up to 30 fragrant flowers. Individual flowers measure slightly over 1 inch. Sepals and petals are white, blotched with lavender at their tips. The lobes of the labellum are folded and completely conceal the column. The midlobe is dark purple, while the side lobes are marked with minute purple spots. The spur is curved upward like a horn, brownish at the tip and light lavender toward the base. The highly fragrant flowers last about 2 weeks.

Aer. odorata, from the high elevations of Chiengmai in northern Thailand, differs somewhat from the southern race described above. The stems are more erect and slightly twisted. Leaves are much shorter, thicker and sturdier, and are curved inward instead of outward. The scape is also sturdier and often less pendulous. The length of the inflorescence and the number and size of flowers are about the same. The flower color is more variable, ranging from white to a lavender tinge to light mauve.

Investigations on chromosome numbers have revealed that members of the northern race are tetraploid with 76 chromosomes, while those of the southern race are diploid with 38 chromosomes. According to Seidenfaden and Smitinand, Kerr referred to the northern race as variety *bicuspidata*.

The plants from northeastern Thailand are also tetraploid, but appear to differ slightly from those of the Chiengmai region in that the stems are stocky, erect and are not twisted ; the leaves are flat and relatively straight, neither drooping nor curving upward ; some produce extremely long inflorescences, up to 18 inches and carrying as many as 50 flowers.

Aerides falcata Ldl.

This orchid is easy to cultivate and flowers freely at low elevations. The stems attain a length of 4 to 5 feet. The leaves are about 10 by $1\frac{1}{2}$ inches. The drooping inflorescence is about 12 inches and carries as many as 30 flowers, usually around April and May. The highly fragrant flowers, about 1 by $1\frac{1}{2}$ inches, open progressively toward the apex and thereby remain decorative for several weeks. The sepals and petals are white, blotched with light lavender toward the tip. The dorsal sepal and petals are curved forward, while the lateral sepals are slightly reflexed. The lip, unlike that of *Aer. odorata* which is folded over the column, is open and showy. The flat midlobe is about $\frac{3}{4}$ inch across, serrated, with a mauve blotch near the apex, while the open side lobes have fine stripes of lavender toward the base. The $\frac{1}{2}$-inch spur is tapered, carried straight forward and hidden directly under the midlobe.

Aer. falcata is widely distributed in Thailand, extending from the northern, northeastern to the eastern, southeastern and southwestern regions. It also occurs in neighboring Indochina and Burma.

Aerides falcata var. *houlletiana* Rchb. f.

Very similar to *Aer. falcata*, this orchid differs in having shorter, broader and thicker leaves, more erect and upright stems and slightly larger, waxy yellow flowers. The general shape of the flower parts are nearly identical to those of *Aer. falcata*. The sepals and petals are light yellow with a touch of lavender toward the tip. The fringed midlobe is cream with a lavender blotch in the apical area. The side lobes have minute lavender spots. This orchid comes from the Korat area in northeastern Thailand. The flowering season is April and May.

Aerides multiflora Roxb.

Aer. multiflora is found in every phytogeographic region of Thailand. It is also distributed in the eastern Himalayas, Burma and Malaysia. The commonly encountered

12

form in Thailand has long, narrow, thick leaves, measuring 10 by 1½ inches. The stem is stout and erect with short internodes. The drooping inflorescence is about 12 inches long, occasionally branched at the base, and bears 50 or more closely spaced flowers during April and May. The flowers are about 1 inch in diameter. Sepals and petals are white, flushed with purple toward the tip, and purple-spotted toward the base. The spade-shaped lip is purple, with a deeper shade toward the center. The side lobes are very small and the spur is short.

A type with more freely branching inflorescences, smaller flowers and broader, thinner leaves is found in the Chiengmai area in northern Thailand.

Aerides flabellata Rolfe

The stem of this species is rather short, with closely spaced leaves, 7 inches by 1 inch. The inflorescence is about 10 inches long and bears 10 to 15 unique and attractive flowers that last about 10 days. The flower is about ¾ by 1¼ inches. Sepals and petals are chartreuse with brown blotches and spots. The broad, fringed lip is white with purple blotches and has a yellow throat. The spur, which is greenish yellow toward the base and olive green at the tip, is somewhat compressed laterally and bent upward at an angle.

This orchid appears to be endemic to the Chiengmai region in northern Thailand. It is a very handsome species but, unfortunately, it does not thrive at low elevations.

Aerides crassifolia Par. & Rchb. f.

The specific name of this orchid is descriptive of the thick and leathery leaves that measure about 5 by 2 inches. The stem is short. The 5-inch inflorescence bears up to 10 flowers during April and May. The mauve flowers are slightly under 2 inches. The dorsal sepal is curved slightly forward, the sides of the lateral sepals are rolled back and the lateral sepals are broad. The midlobe is broadly spade-shaped and dark mauve. The horn-shaped spur is slightly curved under the midlobe. This species comes from northern, northeastern and eastern Thailand and is also found in neighboring Burma.

Aerides mitrata Rchb. f.

At first glance this orchid appears to have terete leaves, but a close examination will reveal that they are deeply channelled. The relatively long leaves, about 18 inches, are drooping. The stem is short. The inflorescence is erect to sub-erect, about 7 inches long and carries about 30 densely spaced, small but fragrant flowers from March to May. Individual flowers measure only ½ inch across. The reflexed sepals and petals are white with purple at the tips. The lip is mauve. The white spur is laterally flattened and pointed forward.

Widely distributed in the Tenasserim Range in Thailand and Burma, this small-flowered but floriferous and handsome species is a worthy addition to any orchid

13

collection.

Aerides hybrids

The first hybrid of *Aerides*, *Aer. affine* X *Aer. fieldingii* was registered as *Aer.* Dominianum by Veitch, nearly 100 years ago. Prior to the Second World War, only 2 other hybrids involving *Aerides* species appeared, but since then more than 70 hybrids have been registered. The majority of the hybrids are *Aeridovanda*, indicating the relative ease in hybridizing *Aerides* and *Vanda* and their close taxonomic relationship. *Aerides* has also been hybridized with *Arachnis*, *Ascocentrum*, *Ascoglossum*, *Neofinetia*, *Phalaenopsis*, *Renanthera*, *Rhynchostylis* and *Vandopsis* to create the generic combinations *Aeridachnis*, *Aeridoglossum*, *Aeridofinetia*, *Aeridopsis*, *Renades*, *Rhynchorides* and *Vandopsides*, respectively.

It is not surprising that the Philippine *Aer. lawrenceae*, generally considered one of the finest *Aerides* species, was used most frequently in hybridization in the past. Within the past decade, however, the majority of the 25 *Aerides* hybrids produced were crosses involving *Aer. odorata*. During this period a hybrid of the unique *Aer. flabellata* appeared for the first time. The successful cross was *Aer. flabellata* X *Ascocentrum curvifolium*. Hybrids involving other *Aerides* species of Thailand have begun to appear.

With the number of fine species of *Aerides* available, the possibilities of improving the horticultural qualities in *Aerides* hybrids appear great. The existence of tetraploid forms of *Aer. odorata* should further add to possible hybrid variations.

ARUNDINA

Arundina, commonly referred to as the bamboo orchid, is widely distributed in Ceylon, the Himalayas, South China, Indochina, Thailand, Malaysia, Indonesia and some of the islands of the Pacific. Several species have been described, but Holttum considers these to belong to a single, highly variable species.

Arundina graminifolia (Don) Hochr.

The flower of this terrestrial orchid resembles a small cattleya. The erect slender stems are 2 to 4 feet high. The leaves are narrow and grasslike. An inflorescence bearing about $2\frac{1}{2}$ — inch flowers arises from the stem apex, usually from October to March. The flowers are produced in succession with one or two open at a time, each lasting only 3 days. The sepals and petals are white to light lavender, while the lip is dark purple at the apex and light purple striped with dark purple in the throat. The lateral sepals are often close together behind the lip.

This orchid, usually inhabiting open areas, is found in most parts of Thailand. It is one of the easiest orchids to culture. In certain parts of Hawaii it has escaped cultivation and is growing abundantly in grassy fields.

Plants can be used effectively in landscape gardening. Liberal amounts of organic matter should be worked into the soil before planting. Because they grow to a height of 4 feet, they should be placed behind shorter plants.

Take care not to bury the crown too deep. When in active growth, the plants should be watered liberally and fertilized occasionally. A healthy plant in cultivation will flower throughout most of the year.

ASCOCENTRUM

The recent trend in hybridizing and cultivating miniature vandaceous orchids has focused considerable attention on the delightful, diminutive *Ascocentrum* species that are common to Thailand. *Asctm. curvifolium* in particular has been hybridized extensively to produce a myriad of color types now available in *Ascocentrum* hybrids.

The genus *Ascocentrum* comprises a few species that are distributed principally through Thailand and Burma. Older classifications placed this group along with *Rhynchostylis* into the heterogeneous *Saccolabium*, but it appears that the separation of *Ascocentrum* into a distinct genus is now generally accepted.

Ascocentrum is represented in Thailand by three species, *Asctm. curvifolium*, *Asctm. miniatum*, and *Asctm. ampullaceum*. A fourth species, *Asctm. micranthum*, which has very small flowers, has recently been removed from *Ascocentrum* and placed in a new genus by Holttum.

The ascocentrums are similar in structure and habit to the strap-leaf vandas except for their reduced size. They are closely related genetically to vandas as further suggested by the relative ease in hybridizing members of the two groups, and by the excellent pairing of chromosomes exhibited by the hybrids.

Ascocentrum curvifolium (Ldl.) Schltr.

This species is the most attractive and consequently the most highly valued within the genus. Its distribution in Thailand is generally limited to the deciduous forests of the mountain ranges bordering Burma in western, northwestern and northern Thailand. The improvement of roads and clearing of forests for cultivation have resulted in its rapid depletion in readily accessible areas. Today, one has to penetrate deep forests near the Burmese border to collect this highly desirable orchid.

Asctm. curvifolium can be easily indentified by the long, recurved, light-green leaves. Purplish spots, which are more prominent during summer, are scattered along the edges of the leaves. The attractive Mars-orange to cinnabarred flowers are about $\frac{3}{4}$ inch across and are borne densely on upright inflorescences 6 to 8 inches long. The petals and sepals are of about equal dimensions and often overlapping, producing a round, full, compact form. The tongue-shaped midlobe of the labellum is about 1/8 inch wide and $\frac{1}{4}$ inch long. The spur is $\frac{1}{2}$ inch long and enlarged at the tip. The anther cap is purplish.

Plants about 6 inches high will produce one or two flower spikes, but larger plants, some as high as 24 inches, may produce as many as seven, which make striking displays during March or April. Individual flowers last about 2 weeks.

16

Teak baskets are generally used for growing this orchid. The lower half of the basket is filled with inch-size charcoal. Then the plants are potted with local fern fibers aligned vertically to facilitate water drainage during the wet monsoon season. This species is easily cultivated, making rapid vegetative growth when grown under lath providing about 50 percent shade. Flowering, however, may be sparse in Bangkok. In years when winter temperatures drop below 60° F for a few weeks, plants will flower profusely.

Ascocentrum miniatum (Ldl.) Schltr.

The specific name, *miniatum*, is descriptive of the diminutive size of this species. The golden-yellow to bright-orange flowers are about 5/8 inch across. The spur is laterally flattened and curved slightly forward. Two or more erect inflorescences, up to 5 inches long, appear during February to April. Individual flowers usually last for 2 weeks. The leaves are compact, fleshy, dark green, channelled and obliquely erect or slightly recurved. Plants may attain a height of 12 inches and produce several lateral branches, but will begin flowering at a height of only 3 inches.

This orchid occurs in practically every phytogeographic region of Thailand, usually in deciduous forests at elevations between 800 to 2500 feet. It is widely distributed from the Sikkim Himalayas through Burma to Java, and even extends to the Philippines. It appears to have wide adaptability and flowers fairly well at low elevations. Consequently, this miniature vandaceous orchid should be a part of most orchid collections.

Plants can be grown in either clay pots or wooden baskets filled with charcoal, fern fiber, or a mixture of both. For those interested in landscaping with orchids, this species will do well attached to trunks or branches of trees. In its native habitat in Thailand, the growing season coincides with the monsoon or rainy season from mid-May to November. Floral initiation generally takes place during the cool, dry months from December to February, with flowering taking place during the hot, dry period from late February to April. Thus, under cultivation it would be advisable to reduce the frequency of watering prior to the normal season of flowering in order to promote floral initiation.

Ascocentrum ampullaceum (Ldl.) Schltr.

The size of the flowers of this species is about equal to that of *Asctm. curvifolium*, but the color is mauve, a refreshing variation in the ascocentrums. Flowers usually appear in April and last about 2 weeks. Twenty or more round, full flowers are carried on erect inflorescences 5 or more inches tall. The midlobe of the labellum is very narrow. The spur, like that of *Asctm. miniatum*, is flattened but curved backward instead of forward. The anther cap is brownish. The dark-green leaves are flat, 6 inches long and 1 inch wide, unevenly notched at the tip, and obliquely erect.

Asctm. ampullaceum is found in northern Thailand and is also distributed in Burma and the Himalayas. It is difficult to grow due to its susceptibility to the leaf and heart-rot disease that commonly afflicts vandas. Like *Asctm. curvifolium*, it requires cool

17

temperatures for floral initiation.

Ascocentrum hybrids

The first hybrid of *Ascocentrum* was registered in 1949 by Dr. C. P. Sideris of Hawaii. This new intergeneric hybrid, which resulted from crossing *Asctm. curvifolium* with *Vanda lamellata*, was named *Ascocenda* Portia Doolittle. Then followed *Ascda*. Meda Arnold (*Asctm. curvifolium* X *V*. Rothschildiana) in 1950, and *Ascda*. Chryse (*Asctm. miniatum* X *V. lamellata*) in 1951, both also produced by Dr. Sideris. It wasn't until 1960 that another hybrid of *Ascocentrum* was registered. However, from 1961 through 1965, 20 *Ascocenda* hybrids appeared, and from 1966 through 1970, 112 new *Ascocenda* hybrids were recorded. During this period numerous ascocendas received the Award of Merit from various orchid societies. Interest in this group of orchids has been maintained due to the many improved characteristics. The *Ascocentrum* species, particularly *Asctm. curvifolium*, in combination with *Vanda* species and hybrids, have given rise to practically all colors from the dark purples and blues to the yellows, oranges and reds in varying shades. Colors are either solid, beautifully tessellated, dotted or even striped. Flowers are full and overlapping. Many are extremely floriferous, producing flower spikes from almost every node throughout the year. Because of these characteristics, the ascocendas are now being cultivated commercially for cut flowers in Thailand.

The majority of ascocendas have involved *Asctm. curvifolium* either directly or in their ancestry. *Asctm. miniatum*, as indicated by its few hybrids, exhibits a dominance of color. Crossed to *V. sanderiana*, some individuals produced attractive yellow flowers, while others produced orange-yellow flowers. Many more hybrids utilizing this species will undoubtedly appear in the near future, due to its transmission of yellow color to its offspring.

Other intergeneric hybrids involving *Ascocentrum* species, most of which were produced only within the last few years, are *Aeridocentrum* (*Aerides* X *Ascocentrum*), *Ascofinetia* (*Ascocentrum* X *Neofinetia*), *Asconopsis* (*Phalaenopsis* X *Ascocentrum*), *Ascorachnis* (*Ascocentrum* X *Arachnis*), *Doricentrum* (*Doritis* X *Ascocentrum*), *Renancentrum* (*Renanthera* X *Ascocentrum*), *Rhynchocentrum* (*Rhynchostylis* X *Ascocentrum*), and *Sarcocentrum* (*Sarcochilus* X *Ascocentrum*). These hybrids have greatly expanded the diversity in vandaceous hybrids.

CALANTHE

Closely allied to *Phaius, Calanthe* is a large group of terrestrial orchids that are widely distributed from South Africa and India through Southeast Asia, eastward to China and Japan, and southward to Australia and Tahiti. Seidenfaden and Smitinand, in *The Orchids of Thailand,* have recorded only 10 species from Thailand but they anticipate a number of additions to this list. This genus can be divided into two groups, one with prominent pseudobulbs and deciduous leaves, the other with relatively small pseudobulbs and persistent evergreen leaves. The deciduous species, although fewer in number than the evergreen species, are nevertheless more attractive and popular. The three deciduous species commonly encountered in Thailand are *Cal. vestita, Cal. rubens* and *Cal. cardioglossa. Cal. vestita* has long been under cultivation in Europe and the United States.

The above three species require similar treatment. The bulbs should be potted just as growth commences from the base, usually around April. A mixture of sand or crushed brick, loam soil and leaf mold or other suitable organic matter should be used. Several bulbs can be placed in a single pot to obtain a good display of flowers. When active growth commences, the plants should be watered copiously and fertilized occasionally. In the fall when the bulbs are mature and the foliage begins to turn yellow and abscise, watering should be reduced. When flower spikes appear, watering should be increased slightly until flowering is completed. After flowering, the plants need a rest. Watering should be drastically reduced and the pots kept in a protected area, or the bulbs can be lifted from the pots, separated and kept in a cool area until new shoots begin to appear. These deciduous calanthes generally require annual repotting for best results.

Calanthe vestita Ldl.

This orchid is the most widely grown and perhaps the finest *Calanthe* species. Twelve or more flowers are borne in graceful sprays, 2 to 3 feet long, usually from November to January. The long-lasting, 2-inch flowers are white except for the yellow throat. The lip is flat, about 1 ¼ inches wide with distinct side lobes and a bilobed midlobe. The spur is 1 inch long and curved under the lip. The pseudobulbs are cone-shaped, 4-to 6-angled and about 4 inches tall, and bear, toward the tip, up to four leaves which mature and abscise around November. This orchid is distributed in South China, Thailand, Malaysia and Indonesia. In Thailand, it is common to the Ranong area of peninsular Thailand.

Calanthe rubens Ridl.

The pseudobulbs of this orchid, unlike those of the above species, are severely constricted toward the middle, and often only a slight pressure on the leaves or upper portion of the pseudobulbs results in breakage at the constriction. The hairy inflorescence, up to 2 feet long, produces around 15 long-lasting flowers in January and February. The flowers are about 1 ½ inches across and 2 inches long. The color of the sepals and petals ranges from lavender tinged to light mauve to dark rose, while the throat of the lip is dark rose. The lateral sepals are reflexed. Like *Cal. vestita*, the lateral lobes of the lip are distinct and the midlobe is bilobed, while the slender spur is curved under the lip. *Cal. rubens* has been collected from the northeast, southeast and peninsular regions of Thailand. It is also native to northern Malaysia. This orchid appears to be easy to cultivate and flower in the lowlands, if a decided rest is given during the dormant period and the other usual care for deciduous calanthes is observed.

Calanthe cardioglossa Schltr.

This small-flowered, deciduous species is relatively common in Thailand. It has been collected from the north, northeast, southeast and peninsular regions. It is difficult to distinguish it from *Cal. rubens* on the basis of vegetative characteristics alone. The flowers, however, are very small and distinctive. The sepals and petals are strongly reflexed, which results in a natural spread of the flower of about ½ inch across. The lip is comparatively large and conspicuous and is darker than the sepals and petals ; often it is attractively spotted. The highly variable color ranges from white to light lavender to deep rose. The spur is about 1 inch long and hangs down. Flowers are produced progressively on an 18-inch scape with two open at a time, usually from December to February. Individual flowers last for only a few days and usually change from lavender or rose to orange or yellow before dropping.

Calanthe hybrids

Calanthe has played a prominent role in the history of orchid hybridization. It has the distinction of having produced the first manmade orchid hybrid, over a century ago. In 1853, John Dominy, in England, crossed two evergreen *Calanthe* species, *Cal. masuca* and *Cal. furcata*. The hybrid was registered in 1856 as *Cal.* Dominy.

The calanthes, particularly the deciduous types, were fairly popular subjects for hybridization in Europe prior to the Second World War. During the nineteenth century as many as 33 *Calanthe* hybrids were registered. From 1900 to 1945, 47 additional hybrids appeared. However, during the period from 1946 to 1970, only 2 hybrids were registered.

Cal. vestita has figured in the greatest number of crosses. One of the most popular hybrids has been *Cal.* Veitchii, a cross between *Cal. vestita* and *Cal. rosea*. Eight hybrids of *Cal. vestita* have appeared, six of which were produced over 60 years ago ; many advanced generation hybrids can be traced back to this species as an early parent.

Cal. rosea, which is also a native of Thailand, is credited with four hybrids, and *Cal. rubens* and *Cal. cardioglossa* with a single hybrid each.

20

COELOGYNE

Coelogyne is a large genus of about 150 species widely distributed in Southeast Asia. The species are highly variable in growth habit, size, shape and color of flowers. Some are beautiful. Thailand is represented by 30 or more species. Unfortunately, the majority grow in high elevations and will not thrive in the hot climate of the lowland tropics. If plants with flower buds already initiated are collected and brought down to low elevations, they will often produce flowers but will rarely flower in subsequent years. The reluctance to flower at low elevations has presented a problem in identifying the species.

Coelogyne cumingii Ldl.

The flowers of this species are produced, usually around March and April, on new growth while leaves are still developing. The 5-inch inflorescence carries three to five flowers which are about 2 inches across. The white sepals and petals are about 1 ¼ inches long and 3/8 inch wide. The lip is also white except for the three long and two short, yellow-crested keels. Edges of the lip are wavy. The leaves are 10 inches long and 1 ¼ inches wide and emerge in pairs from the top of the pseudobulbs. The pseudobulbs are about 1 inch apart, 2 ½ inches long and 1 ¼ inches wide.

Coel. cumingii is found in the peninsular region of Thailand; it is also distributed in Malaysia, Borneo and Sumatra.

Coelogyne virescens Rolfe

This lovely green orchid, also known as *Coel. parishii*, comes from relatively high elevations of northern, northeastern, eastern and southeastern parts of the country, as well as from neighboring Indochina and Burma. The clustered pseudobulbs are characteristically squarish and about 6 inches tall and $\frac{3}{4}$ inch wide. During March and April, the flower spike, which arises from the apex of the pseudobulbs between the two leaves, bears three to five long-lasting flowers 2 inches across. The petals are very narrow and slightly reflexed, with the sepals broader. The light-green midlobe has two lateral black blotches and fine black spots, while the somewhat triangular side lobes are striped with black. A two-crested central keel and two prominent lateral keels extend from the base of the lip to the apical region of the midlobe. The tip of the dark-green, curved column forms a hood over the anther. The persistent bracts turn brown soon after the flowers open.

Coelogyne hybrids

The first hybrid of *Coelogyne* was registered as early as 1906. Brymer crossed

Coel. asperata with *Coel. dayana* and named the hybrid *Coel.* Brymeriana. Between 1906 and 1923, seven other hybrids were produced, but since then, with the exception of a single additional hybrid, *Coel. lawrenceana* X *Coel. mooreana*, registered in 1950, there has been virtually no activity in hybridization in this group.

The limited hybridization with *Coelogyne* perhaps reflects the lack of popularity of this group. With the diversity existent among the 150 or more species, many of which can be considered of horticultural value, it is somewhat surprising that the coelogynes have not become more widely known and cultivated. Perhaps their sparse flowering habit in warmer climates may be a factor. A hybridization program, however, could overcome this problem and bring about additional improvement, as has been demonstrated in other groups of orchids.

CYMBIDIUM

A popular group of orchids, cymbidiums are extensively cultivated for commercial cut flowers. They have been subjected to intensive hybridization, with the result that present-day offsprings are vastly superior to their progenitors. The genus comprises 50 or more species distributed from Madagascar, Ceylon and India throughout Southeast Asia, extending to Japan to the east and Australia to the south. The members of the genus can be grouped into : 1) the large-flowered, terrestrial species such as *Cym. insigne,* 2) the miniature terrestrial species such as *Cym. siamense,* and 3) the epiphytic, warm-climate species with pendulant spikes and small flowers such as *Cym. finlaysonianum.* Eighteen or more species occur in Thailand. However, some are not commonly encountered and some do not flower in the lowlands.

The terrestrial cymbidiums are easy to cultivate. They can be potted in a mixture of loam, or sand, and organic matter which provides good water retention and proper drainage. A mixture of sand, leafmold or sphagnum, and shredded fern fiber is also satisfactory. Potting is preferably done soon after the flowering period. When active growth begins, the plants should be watered regularly and fertilized occasionally. They require temperatures under 60° F for satisfactory floral initiation and development ; consequently, most of the terrestrial cymbidiums of Thailand may flower with difficulty at low elevations.

The epiphytic cymbidiums are very easy to grow and flower. When grown in pots or baskets they should be provided with good aeration and drainage, and hung in order to display the pendulant inflorescences to best advantage. Fern fiber, coconut fiber, crushed bricks, charcoal and similar materials, alone or in combinations, serve as satisfactory media. The plants can tolerate a considerable amount of sunlight.

Cymbidium lowianum Rehb. f.

This handsome terrestrial orchid comes from relatively high elevations of northern Thailand and neighboring Burma. The clustered pseudobulbs are about 3 inches tall, and the leaves are 2 to 3 feet long. From January to March, arching inflorescences produce up to 20 flowers each. The long-lasting flowers measure 4 inches across. The sepals and petals are greenish yellow, faintly streaked with reddish brown, while the lip is creamish white, with a maroon patch bordered by white at the apex.

Cymbidium insigne Rolfe

This is probably the most valuable species of the genus, particularly due to its contribution in producing the improved hybrids of today. It occurs at 4000 to 5000

23

feet elevation in Loei Province in northeast Thailand and in northern Burma. The oval pseudobulbs are 3 inches tall, and the leaves are about 2½ feet long and 1 inch wide. The tall upright spikes, which measure 3 to 4 feet, carry 10 to 20 flowers from December to February. Flowers are about 3 inches across. The sepals and petals of nearly equal size are light rose with a maroon midrib and numerous small spots toward the base. The lip is pale pink with dark maroon stripes and dots, and two yellow keels extending as far as the base of the midlobe. The inner surface of the curved column is finely striped with maroon.

Cymbidium tracyanum Hort. ex O'Brien

Cym. tracyanum is similar in growth habit to *Cym. lowianum* and *Cym. insigne*. It comes from Doi Intanond and Doi Suthep in northern Thailand, at about 4000 feet elevation. The long inflorescence bears up to 15 flowers, measuring 4½ inches across. The relatively narrow sepals and petals are greenish yellow, suffused with brown and with brown broken longitudinal stripes. The dorsal sepal is curved forward and forms a hood over the column and side lobes. The side lobes are yellow striped with brown. The prominent midlobe is creamish yellow spotted with maroon and has wavy margins.

Cymbidium siamense Rolfe ex Downie

This delightfully fragrant and attractive miniature terrestrial orchid is endemic to northern, northeastern and eastern Thailand. It is generally found at elevations above 1000 feet. The pseudobulbs are comparatively small, with leaves about 20 inches long and ½ inch wide. The erect inflorescence is up to 1 foot long, bearing about six flowers, usually from January to April. Individual flowers are 1½ inches across. The petals are slightly under 1 inch long and 3/8 inch wide, and face forward close to each other. The lateral sepals are slightly larger. The dorsal sepal is erect, while the lateral sepals are somewhat reflexed. Both sepals and petals are chartreuse with five reddish stripes. The midlobe is creamish with reddish purple spots. The tip is usually curled under. The rounded side lobes have a red margin and are spotted with red. The pedicel and ovary are 1 inch long, while the bract is only half as long. This orchid is easy to cultivate but, like the large-flowered species, appears to require cool temperatures for flowering.

Cymbidium ensifolium Sw.

This terrestrial miniature cymbidium, occurring in northern and northeastern Thailand, is characterized by its narrow leaves similar to those of *Cym. siamense*. The flower spikes are 24 inches high, carrying 15 to 18 highly fragrant flowers, usually in January. The individual flowers are 2½ inches across the lateral sepals. The petals, which are close together and point forward to form a hood over the column, are 1¼ inches long and 3/8 inch wide and are green, striped with purplish brown. The slightly longer but narrower sepals are flat and spread out and are purplish brown over a greenish base. The severely reflexed midlobe is greenish yellow with purplish brown

24

blotches and greenish edges, while the indistinct side lobes are maroon at the edges. The curved column is yellow-capped, green toward the base, flushed with purplish brown toward the tip, and finely striped on the inner surface.

Cymbidium finlaysonianum Ldl.

This is a very common cymbidium in Thailand, particularly in the peninsular region. Although this epiphyte is seen on various types of trees, it favors the palmyra palm. Wherever large palm groves are found in southern Thailand, numerous plants, from small seedlings to huge clumps, are seen attached to the trunks of this palm. This orchid is also native to Malaysia, Indonesia and the Philippines.

The pseudobulbs are insignificant. The erect leaves are thick and fleshy, unequally bilobed at the tip, and up to 30 inches long and 1 ½ inches wide. The many-flowered pendulant spike is about 2 to 3 feet long. Individual flowers are about 2 inches across the spreading lateral sepals. The petals and sepals are brownish yellow, flushed with purple toward the base. The midvein of the petal is reddish purple. The petals are fairly close to each other in a forward position. The midlobe of the labellum is white with a maroon blotch at the tip and a yellow patch at the base. The tip is curved downward. The side lobes are maroon with white stripes and are as long as the column. Two long, straight crimson keels run down the center of the lip. Flowers are produced from June to November and last for about 2 weeks.

Cymbidium simulans Rolfe

The growth habit of *Cym. simulans* is similar to that of *Cym. finlaysonianum*. The pendulant inflorescences, carrying about 30 flowers each, are usually produced in March and April. The flowers are smaller than those of *Cym. finlaysonianum*, measuring about 1 ¼ inches across the spreading lateral sepals. The sepals and petals are reddish brown, bordered by yellow. The light-yellow midlobe is often striped with purplish red, although sometimes the apical portion is solid purplish red. A bright-yellow patch is found at the base of the midlobe. The side lobes are acute, almost as long as the column and striped with purple. The curved column is dark purple with a conspicuous yellow anther cap. A pure yellow-flowered form is also available. The species is distributed in Burma, Thailand, South China and Indonesia. In Thailand it is found in the northern, northeastern and southwestern regions.

Cymbidium hybrids

The large-flowered cymbidiums have been subjected to intensive hybridization over the years. Up to 1946, more than 1000 hybrids were registered, with the interest in this group remaining unabated up to the present. Relatively few species have been the major progenitors of the present-day hybrids. Both *Cym. insigne* and *Cym. lowianum* have been heavily involved in crosses.

Cym. insigne has been particularly important in the development of the modern

25

hybrids, for it is one of the parents of two outstanding stud plants, *Cym.* Alexanderi 'Westonbirt' (*Cym.* Eburneo-lowianum X *Cym. insigne*) and *Cym.* Pauwelsii 'Compte d'Hemptinne' (*Cym. insigne* X *Cym. lowianum*). *Cym. lowianum* itself has contributed much, for it is the grandparent of the former and the direct parent of the latter stud plants. Both of these cultivars are tetraploids and have played significant roles in the breeding of outstanding polyploid cymbidiums, including *Cym.* Babylon, *Cym.* Balkis, *Cym.* Rosanna and *Cym.* Swallow.

In recent years, hybrids between the large-flowered tetraploids and the diploid miniatures have become popular. The hybrids between the two types are referred to as polymins (polyploids X miniatures). *Cym. pumilum*, a native of China, is probably the finest of the miniatures. Up to 1946, only two hybrids of *Cym. pumilum* were registered. From 1946 through 1960, nine hybrids appeared, but during the period of only 10 years, from 1961 through 1970, 111 hybrids appeared. *Cym. ensifolium* has figured in the production of several polymins, but no hybrids have resulted as yet from *Cym. siamense*, the endemic species of Thailand.

A few hybrids have been obtained with the warm climate, epiphytic species with pendulant inflorescences, including *Cym. simulans* and *Cym. finlaysonianum*, but none has proven to be exceptional.

Dendrobium is one of the largest genera of the Orchidaceae and contains more than 1000 species that are distributed throughout the vast triangular area connecting Japan, India and New Zealand. Thailand is extremely rich in the species of this genus, many of which are highly valued for their horticultural qualities. Seidenfaden and Smitinand, in *The Orchids of Thailand*, enumerated 135 *Dendrobium* species. This list will undoubtedly be expanded. The genus has been subdivided into many sections such as the *Phalaenanthe* (e.g., *Den. phalaenopsis*), *Ceratobium* (e.g., *Den. gouldii*), *Eugenanthe* (e.g., *Den. nobile*), *Latourea* (e.g., *Den. macrophyllum*), *Nigrohirsutae* (e.g., *Den. formosum)* and *Callista* (e.g., *Den. aggregatum*). The great majority of the handsome, cultivated species of Thailand fall into three sections, *Callista*, *Eugenanthe* and *Nigrohirsutae*.

The *Callista* section includes relatively few species that are native to Burma, Thailand and neighboring countries. They are generally characterized by very attractive, compact, arching or drooping inflorescences and sheathless nondeciduous leaves. It is of interest to note that *Den. aggregatum* and *Den. chrysotoxum* have 2n = 38 chromosomes, which is the more common number for *Dendrobium* species, while *Den. thyrsiflorum*, *Den. farmeri* and *Den. densiflorum* have 2n = 40 chromosomes.

The widely distributed *Den. aggregatum* and *Den. farmeri*, inhabiting relatively low elevations, are easy to grow and flower in the lowlands. The other species require cool conditions for best flowering. Plants can be placed in pots or wooden baskets with fern fiber as the medium. They also can be attached to a piece of wood, twig or tree-fern slab. The simplest method of culture is to attach the plants to the trunk or branch of a tree. Plants should be kept relatively cool and dry during the winter to promote flowering.

Dendrobium aggregatum Roxb.

This species can be distinguished easily from the rest of the callistas by its one-leaved pseudobulbs. It is widely distributed in the deciduous forests of Thailand. It grows on trunks or branches of deciduous trees, and is usually exposed to the full sun after the trees shed their leaves in November and December and until these trees send out a new flush of growth in April. The flowering season is usually from March to May.

The clustered pseudobulbs are about 3 inches high and bear solitary dark-green, heavy-textured leaves, measuring 3 inches long and 1 inch wide. The pseudobulbs are plump when young, but with age gradually develop furrows and wrinkles. The

27

pendulant inflorescences arising from the sides of the pseudobulbs are about 7 inches long and carry 20 or more flowers. The petals and sepals are pale to bright yellow and usually deepen in color with age. The labellum is golden yellow. The flowers are delicate and relatively short-lived.

Den. aggregatum can be found in most of the phytogeographic regions of Thailand, and their distribution extends to the Himalayas and Indochina.

Dendrobium chrysotoxum Ldl.

This handsome species occurs in the deciduous forests of Thailand, usually above 2000 feet elevation. It is also distributed in Burma, the Himalayas and Indochina. The pseudobulbs are narrow at the base, gradually thickened toward the middle, then tapered at the tip. They may attain a height of 12 inches and a thickness of 1½ inch. The older bulbs are yellowish. Six to seven leaves, about 7 by 2 inches, are borne near the top of the pseudobulbs. The arching or drooping inflorescences, sometimes as long as 1 foot, may produce 20 or more fragrant and attractive flowers which last about 2 weeks. The individual flowers are about 1½ inches across, with waxy, bright-yellow sepals and petals and a fringed orange-yellow-centered labellum. They usually bloom in April. In Chiengmai, where this species thrives, a magnificent specimen, grown in a wooden basket about a yard in diameter, carried 75 sprays, each with 15 to 20 flowers.

Dendrobium farmeri Paxt.

Holttum, in *Flora of Malaya, I, Orchids*, states that this species is perhaps the most beautiful native Malayan orchid. It is the only *Callista* species native to Malaysia. It has a fairly wide distribution in Thailand and is also found in Burma and the Himalayas.

Individual flowers of the typical species, which measure about 1½ inches across, have roundish, overlapping white sepals and petals. The round labellum is orange-yellow with a white rim. The drooping inflorescence carries up to 20 flowers, loosely arranged. The flowers usually appear in February, ahead of the other callistas. Three or four smooth, thin-textured leaves, 6 by 2 inches, are clustered at the tip of the four-angled pseudobulb.

Considerable variation occurs within the species. A yellow-flowered variety, aureoflava, has been collected from the high elevations of Khanburi forest in western Thailand. The sepals and petals are amber-yellow and the labellum is cadmium-orange. The leaves are thicker, broader and greener than the common type encountered in the Chandhaburi region in southwestern Thailand. This variety flowers from May to July. Plants from the Ranong area in southwestern Thailand produce large flowers that are often tinged with lavender on the outer surfaces. The common type found in the Chandhaburi region has also been referred to as *Den. palpebrae*. However, aside from the variation in flower color, other flower and plant characteristics within the group generally appear to be similar and, therefore, the separation into two species may not be warranted.

28

Dendrobium thyrsiflorum Rchb. f.

This has been one of the most popular *Dendrobium* species of northern Thailand. Although still abundant in its native habitat, in the more accessible areas it will soon become scarce. It is found in somewhat shaded areas at relatively high elevations. The pendulant inflorescences, about 9 inches long, carry 30 to 50 densely arranged flowers. Individual flowers are about $1\frac{1}{4}$ inches across. Sepals and petals are overlapping, white and delicate, while the rounded labellum is a highly contrasting orange-yellow. The flowers are very attractive and have a delicate fragrance, but unfortunately they are short-lived, often lasting only 5 to 7 days.

Unlike the four-angled pseudobulbs of *Den. farmeri*, those of *Den. thyrsiflorum* are long and cylindrical with vertical grooves, and reach a height of 18 inches. The four to six leaves borne toward the tip of the pseudobulb are smooth, flexible, dark green, and measure about 6 by 2 inches.

Dendrobium densiflorum Wall.

Not a common species in Thailand, *Den. densiflorum* occurs at high elevations near the Burmese border. It is also distributed in Burma and the Himalayas, from Nepal to Assam, at elevations above 3500 feet. It is similar to *Den. farmeri* in having four-angled pseudobulbs, but has thicker, rounder, greener leaves and more dense inflorescences of entirely yellow flowers. It does not do well at low elevations.

Callista hybrids

Relatively few hybrids have been produced with the callistas, probably due to sterility factors. Many of the hybrids were produced during the early days of orchid hybridization. Intrasectional hybrids appear to be equally difficult to produce as intersectional hybrids. In *Sanders' List of Orchid Hybrids*, two within-section natural hybrids, *Den. obscurum* (*Den. chrysotoxum* X *Den. thyrsiflorum*) and *Den. farmeri-thyrsiflorum* (*Den. farmeri* X *Den. thyrsiflorum*), are recorded.

Den. chrysotoxum was hybridized with *Den. pulchellum* at the turn of the century. This hybrid, registered as *Den.* Illustre, was backcrossed to *Den. pulchellum* to produce the outstanding *Den.* Gatton Sunray. Recently, *Den.* Gatton Sunray was crossed with *Den. chrysotoxum* to produce *Den.* Golden Swan. Other *Den. chrysotoxum* hybrids which have appeared are *Den.* Caesar X *Den. chrysotoxum* and *Den. formosum* X *Den. chrysotoxum*.

An interesting hybrid of *Den. aggregatum* (*Den. aggregatum* X *Den. undulatum* var. *bromfieldii*), was flowered in 1963. The latter species is a cane-type evergreen orchid with pseudobulbs up to 6 feet high, while those of *Den. aggregatum* are only 3 inches. The offspring exhibited a strong influence of *Den. aggregatum*, for the pendulant flower spikes appeared on 7-inch pseudobulbs. Other *Den. aggregatum* hybrids that have been produced are *Den.* Thomas Warne X *Den. aggregatum*, and *Den. aggregatum* X *Den. superbiens*.

29

DENDROBIUM-EUGENANTHE

The section *Eugenanthe* comprises a large group of species characterized by fleshy pseudobulbs, sheath-bearing deciduous or semideciduous leaves, and medium to large showy flowers. The majority of species make handsome potted plants when in full flower. Species lend themselves well to the production of magnificent specimen plants with a profusion of blooms.

Thirty or more species of this group are available in Thailand. Many inhabit relatively high elevations of the Tenasserim Range and require a cool, dry season to stimulate flowering. They may flower with difficulty when brought to the lowlands of the tropics.

Growth and flowering patterns vary according to the species. In general, however, vegetative growth commences during or soon after flowering, from February to May. Rapid growth ensues during the warm rainy season from late May to October. Leaves turn yellow and drop with the advent of the cool, dry period. In cultivation, it is important to water copiously, fertilize occasionally and provide adequate sunlight and air movement during the period of active vegetative growth. In the fall when growth matures, fertilizing should be discontinued and watering curtailed until flower buds are formed. From then on, the plants should be watered moderately. Species with drooping stems should be grown in baskets or on slabs of wood or tree fern and hung in the shadehouse.

Dendrobium aphrodite Rchb. f.

A rather uncommon species, *Den. aphrodite*, inhabits the Tenasserim Range of Chiengmai in northern Thailand. Seidenfaden and Smitinand encountered a rich stand of this species in a dipterocarp forest near Tak during the Sixth Thai-Danish Expedition of 1968. The sub-erect stems are 6 to 12 inches long and about $\frac{3}{4}$ inch wide. The flowers, produced in February and March, are borne singly or in pairs on 2-to 3-inch scapes and are $2\frac{1}{2}$ inches across. The creamish yellow sepals and petals do not open fully. The large lip is $1\frac{1}{2}$ inches in diameter, notched at the apex and has a few hairs toward the center. It is creamish yellow with two dark-purple blotches at the base. The anther cap is purple and conspicuous.

Dendrobium capillipes Rchb. f.

The clustered pseudobulbs of this dwarf species are about $2\frac{1}{2}$ inches long and $\frac{1}{2}$ inch wide. The leaf blades are deciduous and the leaf sheaths are white. The inflorescence is erect and produces three to four light-yellow flowers about $1\frac{1}{4}$ inches across, usually around February. The petals are broad; the sepals are narrow and short. The large round lip is dark-yellow with light-brown streaks at the base. This orchid is found in the Chiengmai region of Thailand.

Dendrobium chrysanthum Wall.

The attractive deep-golden-yellow flowers of this orchid usually appear in April or May on growths still retaining their foliage. Two to three flowers are borne on very short scapes at the nodes, toward the end of the long pendulant stems. Flowers last about 1 week. Individual flowers measure from 1½ to 2 inches. The sepals and petals are broad, thick and overlapping, and thereby produce a round and full form. The broad, fringed lip has two contrasting dark-maroon blotches. This species is native to the eastern Himalayas, Burma and Thailand. In Thailand it has been collected at high elevations of the Chiengmai and Loei Provinces. It does not do well in the lowlands.

Dendrobium crassinode Bens. & Rchb. f.

The specific name, *crassinode*, refers to the swollen nodes of the pendulant pseudobulbs which attain a length of 12 to 18 inches. Two or three flowers are borne on short scapes at the nodes, from February to April. Flowers are about 2 to 2½ inches across. The sepals and petals are white with purple tips. The velvety white lip has a dark-yellow blotch at the base. It is found in northern Thailand and neighboring Burma.

Dendrobium crepidatum Ldl.

The dainty, delicately fragrant flowers of this orchid measure about 1 inch across. The petals and sepals are waxy and white, tinged with lavender. The round lip is deep yellow with a white edge. The flowers are borne in twos or threes on very short scapes, usually around April. The pseudobulbs are 9 to 15 inches long and semi-erect or curved. The leaf sheaths have characteristic white streaks. This species comes from the mountains of northern and northeastern Thailand. It is also native to Burma, Indochina, China and Assam.

Dendrobium crystallinum Rchb. f.

This fairly common orchid is found in northern, northeastern, western and southwestern Thailand and in neighboring Laos, Cambodia and Burma, as well as in Sikkim Himalaya. The flowers, which measure 2¼ inches across, are produced in pairs on short scapes toward the apical region of the erect to sub-erect pseudobulbs. The sepals and petals are white, blotched with lavender at the tips. The petals are about 1¼ inches long and slightly under ½ inch in width; the sepals are equal in length but narrower in width and reflexed. The lip is 1¼ inches long and ¾ inch wide when flattened, and is cupped, yellow centered and purple tipped. The anther cap on the short green column is characteristically elongate with numerous papils. The flowering season is late April and May.

Dendrobium devonianum Paxt.

This delicate and lovely orchid is found in the mountain ranges of northern and northeastern Thailand and neighboring countries. The sub-erect purplish pseudobulbs are 10 to 15 inches long. Flowers, which last from 10 to 14 days, are produced on short scapes at the upper nodes in twos or threes, during February and March. The individual flower is about 1 ¼ inches in diameter. The sepals and petals are white with lavender tips. The round lip is creamish white with a lavender tip and a bright-yellow center. Minute hairs are found at the margin, and the throat has purple spots and streaks.

Dendrobium dixanthum Rchb. f.

The pseudobulbs are slender and sub-erect, reaching 2 feet in length. As many as five flowers are produced at a node during February and March. The bright buttercup-yellow flowers are about 1 ¼ inches across and relatively thin-textured. The lip is large and conspicuous, finely fringed at the edges and darker yellow than the sepals and petals. This orchid is found in northern, northeastern and western regions of Thailand and in neighboring Burma.

Dendrobium falconeri Hk.

This orchid can be readily identified by its unique vegetative characteristics. The pendulant stems are 2 to 3 feet long, branched, and very thin with swollen nodes. Flowers are solitary, or in twos, and about 2 inches across. The narrow and acute sepals and petals are white with purple tips. The lip is dark maroon in the throat and tipped with purple at the apex. This beautiful orchid is distributed in Assam, northern Burma and northern Thailand. It is very difficult to maintain under cultivation. Plants brought down from their native habitat to low elevations may produce flowers during the first year, but thereafter gradually degenerate. For best success, plants should be grown in a shady, humid, cool spot.

Dendrobium fimbriatum Ldl.

This is one of the more attractive orchids in the *Eugenanthe* group. The stems are 2 to 4 feet high, erect, and produce pendulous inflorescences from the upper portions in February and March. The inflorescences carry up to 15 flowers, each measuring 1 ¾ inches across. The petals and sepals are orange-yellow, and the large, round, fringed lip is deep orange-yellow. The variety *oculatum* has a contrasting dark-maroon blotch in the throat. Both varieties occur in Thailand, although the blotched variety appears to be more prevalent. This fine species is native to Nepal, Burma, Thailand and Indochina. In Thailand it has been found in the western, northern and northeastern regions.

Dendrobium findlayanum Par. & Rchb. f.

The swollen nodes of this orchid serve as a distinguishing characteristic. Actually, the upper half of the internode, up to and including the node, is swollen, with the lower portion drastically reduced in diameter. The stems are about 20 inches tall. Inflorescences, produced from the nodes of the upper portion of the pseudobulb, are about 1½ inches long, each bearing two to three delicately colored flowers measuring about 3 inches across. The sepals and petals are pale lavender or white tinged with lavender. The lip is saffron-yellow in the center and very pale yellow at the edges. This species is considered to be endemic to northern Thailand, but possibly the distribution extends to neighboring Burma.

Dendrobium friedericksianum Rchb. f.

From the Chandhaburi district in southeastern Thailand, comes the highly desirable endemic species, *Den. friedericksianum*. The flowers are fairly large, of good form, attractive and long lasting. Because it inhabits the low elevation forests of southeastern Thailand, it can be cultivated and flowered with greater success in the lowlands than most of its allied species. The stems are sub-erect, up to 20 inches high and 1 inch thick. From January to March, the inflorescence produces three or four flowers about 2¼ inches across. The chrome-yellow petals and sepals are waxy and of good substance. The lip is slightly darker yellow. Some plants have flowers with two maroon blotches in the throat; others do not. Flowers have lasted as long as 5 weeks on the plants.

Dendrobium hercoglossum Rchb. f.

This species, with dainty, light-mauve flowers, is easy to cultivate and flower. It is distributed in southeastern Thailand. The pseudobulbs are somewhat pendulous, about 1 foot long, narrow at the base and thickened to ½ inch toward the upper portion. From February to April the inflorescences carry four or five flowers on the most recent growths, often before the leaves are shed completely. The flat, well-shaped flowers are about 1 inch across. The sepals and petals are acute. The hollow lip has a hairy callus at the base of the midlobe, which is triangular and mauve colored toward the tip. The dark-purple anther is conspicuous against the pale-mauve sepals and petals. *Den. linguella*, a closely related species, occurs in peninsular Thailand and is widely distributed in Malaysia. It differs slightly from *Den. hercoglossum* in its longer mentum, and the stems which have the same thickness throughout.

Dendrobium heterocarpum Ldl.

A highly variable species, *Den. heterocarpum* has also been known as *Den. aureum*. It is widely distributed from Ceylon, northern India, Burma, Thailand, through Malaysia to the Philippines. In Thailand it is found in several phytogeographic regions. Although such pseudobulb variations as erect and pendulant, thick and thin, short and long are known for this species, the type generally encountered in Thailand has erect to sub-erect pseudobulbs up to 18 inches long and ½ inch thick. Fragrant flowers, about 2½ inches across, are produced in twos and threes from late December to February. The relatively narrow and pointed sepals and petals are creamish yellow,

33

while the lip is darker yellow except for the creamish apical portion, and is centrally blotched with purplish brown and striped with purplish brown in the throat. The flowers are well proportioned, and plants with profuse blooms make excellent decorative pieces.

Dendrobium lituiflorum Ldl.

The slender pendulous stems, about 20 inches long, produce a profusion of attractive blooms in March. Two flowers, up to $2\frac{1}{2}$ inches across, are produced at a node. The sepals are mauve ; petals are a deeper mauve. The trumpet-shaped lip is white with a purple base and margin. This orchid is native to Assam, Burma and Thailand, at relatively high elevations.

Dendrobium moschatum Sw.

The stems of this orchid are erect to sub-erect and attain 5 feet or more in length. The basal region of the young stem is purple, spotted with green. The leaves are about 5 by $1\frac{1}{2}$ inches, glossy, smooth, thin and pliable. About 10 attractive flowers are carried on pendulant sprays from the upper portions of the stem, usually in March and April. The flowers are about $2\frac{1}{2}$ inches across and of good form. The sepals and petals are light orange ; the cup-shaped, fringed lip is darker orange with two maroon blotches in the throat. This fine form occurring in Thailand is the variety *cupreum*. The type species is pale yellow with purplish veins or a purple flush. The species is native to the Himalayas, Burma, Laos and Thailand. It inhabits medium to high elevations of northern, northcentral, southeastern and western Thailand. In the Khanburi and Pitsanuloke areas, numerous plants have been observed growing on relatively exposed surfaces of large boulders. In the dry season the leaves turn purplish red. Plants do well in nearly full sun. It is easy to cultivate and will flower occasionally in the lowlands.

Dendrobium nobile Ldl.

The most popular member of the *Eugenanthe* section, *Den. nobile*, has been cultivated and hybridized for more than a century. It is a highly variable species, and numerous botanical as well as horticultural varieties exist. The stems are erect, from 12 to 18 inches high and 1 inch thick. During March and April, two to four flowers are produced at a node, usually on leafless pseudobulbs. The flowers are about $2\frac{1}{2}$ inches across. The sepals and petals are often white toward the base and lavender toward the tip. The lip is purple in the throat, with a yellow or white border and a purple edge. Several color variations exist. Flowering plants make glorious displays under suitable environmental conditions. Unfortunately, it is difficult to flower at low elevations in the tropics, although it will produce flowers occasionally if kept relatively dry during the winter months. This orchid species is distributed from the Himalayas through Burma, Thailand and Laos to South China. Its habitat in Thailand is in the mountains of the northern and northeastern regions.

34

Dendrobium parishii Rchb. f.

The pseudobulbs of this orchid are unevenly curved and up to 12 inches long. Often the nodal area is slightly swollen. The highly scented flowers are 1½ to 2 inches across and are borne in twos or threes on short scapes from the apical nodes in April and May. The dark-lavender sepals and petals are of good substance. The lip is hairy and bears two dark-purple blotches. This species is found in northern Thailand as well as in neighboring Burma, Laos and Cambodia.

Dendrobium pierardii Roxb.

The species produces small, delicate flowers in abundance on long pendulant stems and lends itself well to the production of spectacular specimen plants. The slender hanging stems are 2 to 5 feet long. The flowers, which measure 2 inches across, are produced in pairs at the nodes around April and May. The sepals and petals are light mauve. The width of the petals is approximately twice that of the sepals. The hairy lip is pale yellow lined with purple at the base. This species is widely distributed from the Himalayas, Burma, Thailand and Indochina to Malaysia. In Thailand it has been found in nearly every phytogeographical region. It can be easily cultivated and flowered successfully.

Dendrobium primulinum Ldl.

Den. primulinum is similar to *Den. pierardii* but the stems are slightly shorter and thicker. The petals and sepals are narrow and of equal dimensions, with the large lip much wider than it is long. Flowers, about 2 inches across, are often borne singly at the nodes, around March. The sepals and petals are light mauve, and the hairy lip is light yellow, veined with purple. Its distribution is similar to that of *Den. pierardii*.

Dendrobium pulchellum Roxb.

Commonly known as *Den. dalhousieanum*, this orchid is widely distributed from the Himalayas to Burma, Thailand, Indochina and Malaysia. A relatively common species in Thailand, it is found in abundance in the open deciduous forests of the northern, northeastern and western regions. The stems are 3 to 5 feet high, up to ¾ inch thick, and erect. The leaf sheaths are characteristically striped with purple. From March to April, pendulous inflorescences are produced on the apical portion of mature leafless stems. They carry about 10 large, handsome flowers, measuring 4 inches across. The broad, waxy sepals and petals are pale yellow, often tinged with lavender in the back. The lip is cupped, hairy and fringed, and has two conspicuous dark-maroon patches. Because the concave lip projects forward, the best view of the flowers is from above. This orchid is relatively easy to cultivate. It can stand a considerable amount of sunlight.

Dendrobium senile Par. & Rchb. f.

The deciduous pseudobulbs, which measure 2 to 4 inches, are characterized by the white, wooly hair on the leaf sheaths. From January to March, one or two flowers, about 1 $\frac{1}{2}$ inches across, are produced in the apical nodes. The nicely proportioned sepals and petals are straw-yellow; the triangular, flat, spade-shaped lip is straw-colored toward the periphery and chartreuse toward the center, with brown lateral stripes toward the base. This orchid is distributed in northern Thailand at high elevations and in adjoining Burma and Laos. It requires a relatively cool climate for satisfactory cultivation.

Dendrobium tortile Ldl.

The erect to sub-erect stems, about 12 to 15 inches high, are thickened and slightly flattened toward the middle. The flowers, about 3 inches across, are produced from the apical nodes in groups of two or three. The narrow, twisted, lilac-mauve sepals and petals are the distinguishing features of this orchid. The lip is pale yellow with purple veins toward the base. This is a native of lower Burma, northwestern, western and peninsular Thailand, and Malaysia. It is easy to cultivate and will flower in the lowlands.

Dendrobium wardianum Warner

This appears to be a larger form of *Den. crassinode*. The pendulous stems are 2 to 4 feet long and about 1 inch thick at the nodes. The flowers are 3 to 4 inches across. The petals measure about 2 by 1 $\frac{1}{4}$ inches, and the sepals are of equal length but slightly narrower. Both are white with purple at the tips. The lip is white with dark yellow toward the base and purple toward the tip, with maroon blotches on both sides. The flowering season is January to March. It is native to Assam, Burma and Thailand. Holttum, in *Flora of Malaya, I, Orchids* considers this one of the finest Burmese dendrobiums.

Eugenanthe hybrids

The species and hybrids of the *Eugenanthe* section enjoyed considerable popularity in Europe during the latter half of the nineteenth century and the early part of the twentieth century. The number of species hybrids registered during this period reflects this popularity. The first hybrid involving species of *Eugenanthe* was *Den.* Dominianum (*Den. linawianum* X *Den. nobile*), which was registered as early as 1864. Up to the year 1900, 41 hybrids were registered, and from 1900 to 1930 an additional 54 hybrids were produced. During the past 40 years, however, *Eugenanthe* species were involved in producing only about 25 hybrids. The species used frequently in crosses were *Den. nobile, Den. primulinum, Den. pulchellum, Den. wardianum* and *Den. findlayanum*.

By far the most important and widely hybridized species has been *Den. nobile*. The species and its improved hybrids have been cultivated extensively over the years in commercial nurseries for potted plant and cut flower sales. The more recent intensive hybridization among advanced polyploid hybrids in Japan has produced remarkably improved types.

36

Relatively few intersectional hybrids have been produced with species of the *Eugenanthe* section. Perhaps the most outstanding intersectional hybrid to appear is *Den.* Gatton Sunray (*Den. pulchellum* X *Den.* Illustre), a plant of which was awarded a First Class Certificate by the Royal Horticultural Society. This cross was registered in 1919. *Den.* Illustre is a hybrid of *Den. chrysotoxum* of the *Callista* section and *Den. pulchellum*. *Den. pulchellum* was also successfully crossed with *Den. thyrsiflorum* of the *Callista* section, *Den. veratrifolium* and *Den. schulleri* of the *Ceratobium* section, and *Den. dearei* of the *Nigrohirsutae* section. Other intersectional hybrids registered are *Eugenanthe* X *Callista* (*Den. nobile* X *Den. thyrsiflorum* and *Den. nobile* X *Den. suavissimum*), *Ceratobium-Phalaenanthe* X *Eugenanthe* (*Den.* Louis Bleriot X *Den. friedericksianum*), and *Phalaenanthe* X *Eugenanthe* (*Den. phalaenopsis* X *Den. primulinum*).

Such horticulturally desirable species as *Dendrobium formosum* and *Den. infundibulum* from Thailand and *Den. dearei*, *Den. sanderae* and *Den. schuetzei* from the Philippines are included in the section *Nigrohirsutae* of the genus *Dendrobium*. The black or brownish hair present throughout the leaf sheaths characterizes this section. The large, handsome and relatively long-lasting flowers of some of the species are important horticultural attributes.

The *Nigrohirsutae* section contains about 35 species distributed in the Himalayas and Southeast Asia. Thailand is represented by 12 or more species, but only a few are generally known to orchidists. Both *Den. formosum* var. *giganteum* and *Den. cruentum*, which come from low elevations in southwestern and peninsular Thailand, respectively, are easy to cultivate and flower in the lowlands. On the other hand, *Den. infundibulum*, *Den. scabrilingue* and *Den. sutepense*, which inhabit high elevations, are difficult to grow. Plants generally do well in pots or baskets with coarse fern fiber as the medium.

Dendrobium formosum Roxb.

This is the most popular and widely cultivated *Nigrohirsutae* of Thailand. It is distributed from the Himalayas to Burma and Thailand. The large-flowered variety, which occurs in abundance in the Ranong region in southwest Thailand, is *Den. formosum* var. *giganteum*. The flowers of this orchid, which measure as much as 4 inches across, are borne in twos or threes on short inflorescences, usually from October to December. The white sepals and petals are of good substance. The lip is white with a golden blotch in the throat, indented at the apex and lacking distinct side lobes. The delicately scented flowers last about 2 weeks. The plants attain a height of 20 inches, although they tend to be shorter and stockier when grown in the open. The leaves are $3\frac{1}{2}$ inches long and $1\frac{1}{4}$ inches wide.

Dendrobium infundibulum Ldl.

The lovely paper-white flowers of this orchid are about $3\frac{1}{2}$ inches across and slightly smaller than those of *Den. formosum* var. *giganteum*. One or two flowers are borne on very short scapes toward the tip of the pseudobulbs, usually from January to March. The lip is blotched with cadmium-orange in the throat, sharply indented at the apex and serrated at the edges. The mentum is relatively long and brown-tipped. Although petals and sepals are thin-textured, the flowers often last more than a month. The long, thin pseudobulbs are about 18 inches tall and often less than $\frac{1}{2}$ inch wide. The leaves are green, thin and flexible.

This orchid inhabits the Tenasserim Range, generally at elevations above

4000 feet, in relatively dense, moist surroundings. Brought down to the low elevation of Bangkok, plants flower during the first season but, subsequently, wither and die.

Dendrobium sutepense Rolfe ex Downie

From the relatively high mountains of Chiengmai comes *Den. sutepense*, an endemic species. The flowers are small, measuring only 1 inch across. The glossy white sepals and petals are narrow and tapered. The midlobe is acute, reflexed and fringed at the edge, and has a raised yellow disc in the center. The side lobes are lined with yellow. One or two flowers are borne on short inflorescences in February and March. The pseudobulbs are slender, about 9 inches tall, and bear four or five leaves measuring 2½ inches by ½ inch.

Dendrobium scabrilingue Ldl.

This delightfully fragrant orchid grows at high elevations in northern, northeastern and eastern Thailand. The flowers are small for the group, measuring only 1½ inches across, but their distinct and pleasing fragrance makes them a favorite of Chiengmai maidens. The 6 by ½ inch pseudobulbs, bearing several short inflorescences of two to five flowers each, are generally cut at the base and worn in the hair or placed in a bowl of water for home decoration. The flowering season begins in late December and ends in February. Individual flowers last more than 5 weeks, and, since buds keep opening over a period of time, plants may remain in excellent display and fragrance for more than 2 months.

The petals and sepals are white, waxy and of good substance. The midlobe of the labellum is light yellow to orange, acuminate, and somewhat reflexed, while the inner surfaces of the angular side lobes are striped with green. The column is light green.

Dendrobium draconis Rchb. f.

Widely distributed in Thailand, particularly along the Tenasserim Range, this species is also found in neighboring Burma and Indochina. It prefers a cool climate for best growth and flowering but is not as exacting in its requirement as *Den. infundibulum*. Although it does not thrive in the lowlands, it will survive and even produce flowers when winter temperatures drop to the low sixties. It usually flowers during March and April, and individual flowers last for about 3 weeks.

Short inflorescences bear two to five flowers, measuring 2 inches across. The glossy white petals and sepals are narrow, tapered and reflexed. The midlobe of the labellum is also tapered and reflexed and has a wavy margin. The throat is bright red. The spur is long, narrow and tubular.

Dendrobium cariniferum Rchb. f.

This species is similar to *Den. draconis* in its distribution, habitat and general requirement for growth and flowering. In Chiengmai Province it can be found

39

growing together with *Den. draconis*. It is also distributed in Assam and northern Burma. Flowers are about 2 inches across. The petals and sepals are creamish yellow and slightly darker toward the tips. The sepals are keeled along the midvein on the outer surface. The midlobe is creamish yellow, while the reflexed side lobes are darker yellow and the throat is reddish orange. The long, tapered and curved spur is brownish purple. The ovary is three-angled. The flowering season is similar to that of *Den. draconis*.

Dendrobium bellatulum Rolfe

The attractive, small-flowered species occupies the same habitat as *Den. draconis* and *Den. cariniferum* in northern Thailand, at an elevation of about 4000 feet. It also is found in Phu Kradung in northeast Thailand as well as in southwest China. The clustered pseudobulbs are about 3 inches tall and ¾ inch wide, narrow at the base, thickened at the center and tapered toward the tip, and bear three to four leaves at the tip. The leaves are grayish green, 1½ inches by ¾ inch and unequally lobed at the tip. Black hair covers the leaf sheaths. The short flower spikes arise at the nodes, from the midsection to the tip of the pseudobulbs, and usually produce one and occasionally two flowers, each measuring 1½ inches across. The creamish-white sepals and petals are of good substance. The lip is distinctly three-lobed with five keels, three of which end in the midlobe to form a papillous crest. The midlobe is a colorful cadmium-orange, relatively broad, bilobed, and heavy textured. The lateral lobes are small and rounded and the throat is scarlet. The spur is saccate. The flowering season is January to March.

Dendrobium margaritaceum Finet

Den. margaritaceum is very similar to *Den. bellatulum* and even occupies the same habitat. The major distinguishing features are the color and keels of the labellum and the season of bloom. The midlobe of the labellum of *Den. margaritaceum* is white with a yellow to red center, while that of *Den. bellatulum* is uniformly yellow. The three keels of *Den. margaritaceum* are more distinct than those of *Den. bellatulum*. *Den. bellatulum* flowers during January to March ; *Den. margaritaceum* flowers during the rainy season from June to August.

Dendrobium cruentum Rchb. f.

This delightful species, with light-green petals and sepals and a highly contrasting bright-red lip, is endemic to peninsular Thailand, slightly farther south than the habitat of *Den. formosum* var. *giganteum*. Plants can be found on small trees in open forests at relatively low elevations. The slender pseudobulbs attain a height of 14 inches. Leaves are only 2 inches long and about ¾ inch wide. One to three flowers are produced on short inflorescences along the upper half of the pseudobulb. Individual flowers measure about 1¼ inches across. The sepals and petals are light green with darker green veins. The petals are very narrow and tapered, while the lateral sepals are broad at the base, tapering to a sharp point. The lip is distinctly three-lobed. The midlobe is fleshy and stiff, acute and reflexed, with somewhat wavy, red side margins. Five bright-red keels are banded at the base of the lip. The two outermost keels are high but short, while the three central keels are low toward the base and end in a tall crest at the center of the midlobe. The lateral lobes are pointed and curved forward, flushed with red and white-tipped. The column is short and light green, and the column foot is red. The mentum is blunt.

When brought to Bangkok, this orchid has flowered continuously throughout the year, with individual flowers lasting slightly more than a month. With its natural habitat at low elevations of peninsular Thailand, it can be expected to grow well in tropical areas. Its attractive, though small, flowers, its continuous flowering habit, and its apparent ease of culture make this little-known member of the *Nigrohirsutae* a worthy one for cultivation. Furthermore, these fine attributes should be of value in a hybridization program.

Dendrobium trigonopus Rchb. f.

Another inhabitant of northern Thailand is the rather uncommon *Den. trigonopus*, which the Thai refer to as *Kam Pak Gai* (golden beak of a chicken). It is also distributed in Laos and neighboring southwestern China. The pseudobulbs are about 5 inches long and ¾ inch wide, purplish brown and wrinkled. The leaves are 3½ inches by 1 inch and clustered at the tip of the pseudobulbs. The sheaths are covered with brownish hairs. The inflorescence, arising from the upper portion of the pseudobulb, is short and carries two or three flowers in February and March. The flowers are slightly under 2 inches across. The straw-yellow sepals and petals are waxy, thick and tapered. The labellum is three-lobed. The midlobe is yellow with a greenish center, while the side lobes are chartreuse with brown stripes.

Nigrohirsutae hybrids

The Philippine species have produced some outstanding intrasectional *Nigrohirsutae* hybrids, such as *Den.* Thomas Warne (*Den. sanderae* X *Den. schuetzei*) and *Den.* Jane Warne (*Den. dearei* X *Den. schuetzei*). *Den. formosum*, which is common to Thailand, has also figured in the production of an excellent hybrid, *Den.* Nelly Sander (*Den. formosum* X *Den. dearei*). It also was hybridized with *Den. lowii* and *Den. ovipostoriferum* of the same section, and several others belonging to different sections. Other hybrids made to date with *Nigrohirsutae* species common to Thailand are *Den. infundibulum* X *Den. dearei*, *Den. infundibulum* X *Den. sanderae*, *Den. draconis* X *Den. dearei*, *Den.* Jaquelyn Thomas X *Den. draconis*, and *Den.* Alison X *Den. cruentum*.

Den. infundibulum, despite its poor adaptability to the low elevations in the tropics, may serve a useful purpose in breeding due to its attractive, long-lasting flowers. Crosses with such large-flowered species as *Den. formosum* var. *giganteum* and the Philippine *Den. sanderae* may possibly result in hybrids with the desirable combination of large, attractive and long-lasting flowers and wide adaptability. *Den. scabrilingue* should play a role in imparting its delightful fragrance to its offspring, while *Den. cruentum* might contribute toward floriferousness and long-lasting, attractively colored flowers.

The three Philippine species, *Den. dearei*, *Den. sanderae* and *Den. schuetzei*, have 40 chromosomes, while, with the exception of the 40-chromosomed *Den. cruentum*, the Thailand species investigated cytologically show 38 chromosomes. The Philippine species are closely related to each other, as evidenced by the regularity in pairing of chromosomes in the hybrids. On the other hand, the hybrid of *Den. formosum* and *Den. dearei* has a number intermediate between the two parents (2n = 39). Chromosome pairing is irregular in the hybrid, indicating a distal relationship of the parental species, and poor fertility of the hybrid.

DENDROBIUM–OTHER SECTIONS

The horticultural species of dendrobiums of Thailand are predominantly confined to the sections *Callista*, *Nigrohirsutae* and *Eugenanthe*. The numerous remaining species, which are classified into 10 or more different sections, are mainly of botanical interest. However, with the present trend toward growing minatures, undoubtedly many of these botanicals will receive attention by orchidists. Two species, *Den. delacourii* of the section *Stachyobium*, and *Den. secundum* of the section *Pedilonum*, may by attractive enough to be considered of horticultural value.

Dendrobium delacourii Guill.

This orchid, when in bloom, is reminiscent of a yellow-flowered orchid of the *Ceratobium* section, except for its reduced size. The erect stems are 10 to 18 inches high and ½ inch thick and carry about 12 leaves, 3½ by 1½ inches, which drop in early winter. Several spikes are produced from the terminal and apical portions of the current season's growth, usually in June and July while the leaves are still fresh and green. The individual spikes are about 6 to 8 inches long and produce up to 20 flowers. The flowers are about 1 inch across. The petals and sepals are pale yellow. The petals are narrow and slightly broadened at the tip. The brown-striped midlobe of the lip is fringed with cilia or long hairs. The brownish-yellow lateral lobes of the lip are folded over the column. The flowers often last for a month. A well-established plant will produce as many as five spikes per growth and makes a fine indoor decoration piece.

A dwarf form of the species, with fleshy pseudobulbs only 1 to 2 inches tall, is commonly encountered. Its flower size and shape are nearly identical to those of the taller type, but the spikes are not as long and do not carry as many blossoms.

Den. delacourii (syn. *Den. ciliatum*) is a common orchid distributed in every phytogeographic region except peninsular Thailand. It also occurs in neighboring Burma and Indochina. It is relatively easy to cultivate and flowers well in the lowlands.

Dendrobium secundum Ldl.

Although individual flowers of this orchid are small, their attractive color and dense arrangement in the inflorescence provide some decorative value. The upright pseudobulbs are up to 2 feet tall and about ¾ inch thick. The leaves drop around the beginning of the cool, dry period when flower buds begin to form. From February to April, inflorescences that are 2 to 4 inches long appear in a horizontal position, with the flowers generally facing up in rows. The individual flowers are tubular, about ¼ inch wide and ¾ inch long. The petals and sepals are rose-purple and the lip is orange-yellow. The mentum is long and curved.

Den. secundum, one of the most common species in Thailand, is found in abundance in practically every phytogeographic region. It is also widely distributed geographically from the Himalayas through Burma, Thailand and Indochina to Malaysia and the Philippines. Having such a wide distribution, this orchid can be expected to have wide adaptability. Those plants, occupying low elevation forests of peninsular Thailand, should be well adapted for culture at low elevations in the tropics. Plants can stand a great amount of sunlight and should be provided a period of rest soon after the growing season.

The unique flower color and arrangement of the inflorescence make it a worthwhile orchid to grow. Unfortunately, flowers are rather short-lived.

DORITIS

Doritis, a genus closely related to *Phalaenopsis*, comprises only a few species. The exact number has not been established due to the confusion which exists in its taxonomy. The highly variable *Doritis pulcherrima*, which abounds in Thailand, has undergone several changes in nomenclature over the years. Lindley first described it in 1833. In 1874, Reichenbach, without knowledge of Lindley's earlier work, named it *Phalaenopsis esmeralda*. Then in 1917, Rolfe came across Lindley's original painting and, because of priority and sufficient differences, retained the separate genus and accepted the name *Doritis pulcherrima*. Later, both J. J. Smith and Holttum treated it as a member of the *Phalaenopsis* genus. Meanwhile, orchidists had adopted the name *Phalaenopsis esmeralda*, and this orchid was so designated in Sander's *List of Orchid Hybrids* for many years. Finally in 1958, the name was changed to *Doritis pulcherrima*, and its hybrids with *Phalaenopsis* to *Doritaenopsis*. Holttum, in 1963, accepted the genus *Doritis* and recognized two species, *Dor. pulcherrima* and *Dor. regnieriana*.

Doritis pulcherrima Ldl.

This orchid is widely distributed in Indochina, Burma, Thailand, Malaysia and Sumatra. In Thailand, it has been found in just about every phytogeographical region. It often grows in sandy soils in the shade of bushes or shrubs. The growth habit is erect. Side shoots are common, and a plant undisturbed in its natural habitat often forms a huge clump consisting of 10 or more growths. The leathery leaves are long and pointed or rounded, green to purplish green, and measure 2 to 6 inches long and 1 to $2\frac{1}{2}$ inches wide. The flowering season is from June to December, but some plants will continue to flower for nearly a year. The erect to sub-erect inflorescences are sometimes branched and measure up to 20 inches, often bearing 20 to 30 flowers. A great many more flowers are borne if the flowering period is prolonged. Individual flowers measure about 1 inch across. The broad base of the lateral sepal is attached to the column foot, and the three-lobed labellum is hinged to the column foot. A pair of narrow appendages appear near the base of the side lobes.

The color of the sepals and the petals ranges from white to light lavender to amethyst-purple. The midlobe also varies in intensity of color but is invariably darker than the sepals and petals. The side lobes vary from light lavender to yellow to brown. The sepals and petals may be greatly reflexed, moderately reflexed, or nearly flat, and the dorsal sepal may even be hooded. Plants inhabiting Prachuab and Huahin near peninsular Thailand are generally highly variable in flower color, ranging from near white to dark purple. On the other hand, plants from certain areas of Prachinburi in eastern Thailand are more uniformly dark purple, and the petals and sepals are not as reflexed.

45

Plants are relatively easy to cultivate and flower. Since in nature they are often found in sandy, well-drained soil with an accumulation of organic debris, such materials as crushed rock, crushed brick, charcoal, fern fiber and other organic media. either alone or mixed in various combinations, can serve as planting media. A mixture of small charcoal pieces and crushed brick in equal amounts has proved satisfactory in Bangkok. As long as the medium is well drained and well aerated, liberal watering during the dry season will keep the plants in a healthy state. It is important, however, to provide good aeration and drainage during the rainy season to prevent bacterial soft rot and the fungus crown rot. Frequent applications of fungicides should minimize the incidence of troublesome diseases.

Doritis pulcherrima var. buyssoniana

From northeastern Thailand, near the banks of the Mekong River in Ubol, comes a larger type of *Dor. pulcherrima* which the Thai refer to as *Daeng Ubol* (Ubol Red). This is Reichenbach's *Phal. buyssoniana,* which is now considered a variation of *Dor. pulcherrima* distinctive enough to warrant a botanical variety status. It appears to be endemic to the Ubol area.

This variety has been established as a tetraploid with $2n = 76$ chromosomes. It has the "gigas" characteristics common to tetraploids. The large, thick, leathery leaves are often spotted with purple on the upper surfaces and suffused with purple on the lower surfaces. The inflorescence is sturdy and erect and attains a height of about 45 inches. The flowers are almost twice the size of the diploid variety and are not generally reflexed. The petals and sepals are of heavy substance, broad, and sometimes overlapping to form a round, full flower. Color ranges from light lavender to dark purple. The flowering season is usually short, from June to August, with the peak in July, but occasionally a few stragglers are seen as late as October, and even later in Chiengmai.

This orchid grows among grasses, in the open among rocks or in sandy soils rich in humus. Ubol, in northeast Thailand, has a relatively low rainfall and a long dry period. The last rains come in late October and, except for an occasional thunderstorm, it is dry from November to mid-May. The winter temperatures are fairly cool. During the hot, dry months from March to May, the plants often shed their leaves. With the advent of the rainy season, they begin active growth and immediately send out a flowering spike. Brought down to the lowlands, they do not fare well. They are highly susceptible to the bacterial soft-rot disease. Flowering is sparse unless the winter temperatures drop to the fifties.

Doritis hybrids

The first hybrid of *Dor. pulcherrima* was registered as *Phal.* Asahi by Iwasaki of Hawaii as early as 1923. The parents were *Dor. pulcherrima* (*Phal. esmeralda*) and *Phal. lindeni.* It was not until about 30 years later, in 1955, that another *Doritis* hybrid appeared. Since then, however, numerous hybrids have been introduced. The majority of these have been registered within the last decade. Several hybrids have shown excellent horticultural qualities. Among them, *Doritaenopsis* **Red** Coral, a result of crossing *Dor. pulcherrima* var. *buyssoniana* and *Phal.* Doris, both tetraploids, has been outstanding, as attested to by several award-winning plants of this progeny.

Primary, or first generation, diploid *Doritaenopsis* hybrids are sterile or of very low fertility, due to the difference in the chromosomal makeup. Although the basic chromosome number of the parental species is identical ($2n = 38$), the chromosomes of *Doritis* are nearly three times the size of those of the *Euphalaenopsis* group. Pairing between *Doritis* and *Phalaenopsis* chromosomes at meiosis is poor, and impaired fertility results.

Variations in chromosome numbers are common in advanced generation *Phalaenopsis* hybrids. If the diploid *Dor. pulcherrima* is crossed with a diploid *Phalaenopsis*, a diploid hybrid progeny results; if crossed with a tetraploid *Phalaenopsis*, a triploid progeny can be expected. Both dipliod and triploid hybrids are low in fertility because of the lack of chromosome homology in the diploid and the lack of homology and chromosome imbalance in the triploid hybrid. If the tetraploid *Dor. pulcherrima* var. *buyssoniana* is crossed with a tetraploid *Phalaenopsis*, the fertility in the hybrid should be enhanced, for the tetraploid hybrid will then consist of two sets each of *Phalaenopsis* and *Doritis* chromosomes. This has been borne out by the success in obtaining second-generation hybrids utilizing *Doritaenopsis* Red Coral.

An understanding of the cytology of the two groups of orchids is of great value in a hybridization program, particularly since hybrid sterility is often encountered. The circumvention of this sterility may be possible through obtaining two sets of chromosomes each of *Doritis* and *Phalaenopsis*.

47

GASTROCHILUS

Gastrochilus is a genus comprising a few species. Seidenfaden and Smitinand listed eight species of Thailand that are classifiable into three sections. Only three species, all belonging to the same section, may be considered worthwhile cultivating for their approximately inch–sized, rather attractive, long–lasting flowers.

Plants are relatively easy to grow. The easiest and most satisfactory method of culture is to attach the plants to a fern slab and place them in an area with relatively light shade.

Gastrochilus dasypogon (Ldl.) O. Kze.

This species is distributed from the Himalayas to Thailand. Not an uncommon species in Thailand, it is known to occur in northern Chiengmai and eastern Nakornnayok, Prachinburi and Aranya Prathet. It usually flowers from October to December on short inflorescences, each bearing from 5 to 10 flowers on the underside of the foliage. The flowers do not resupinate as most orchids do, and the complex lip of the flowers oriented to the axis renders an attractive ball-like inflorescence. The individual flowers are about 1 inch across. The creamish to greenish yellow to yellow petals and sepals are about $\frac{1}{2}$ inch long and rather narrow. The sac of the lip is purple at the rim and orange-yellow at the base. The midlobe is fringed. The highly fragrant flowers last about 1 month. The unequally toothed leaves are about 6 by $1\frac{1}{2}$ inches. The stem is very short.

This species is very similar to Gastr. calceolaris, which has slightly smaller flowers with a midlobe that is hairy except for the fleshy orange-yellow central disc.

Gastrochilus bellinus (Rchb. f.) O. Kze.

From the relatively high elevations of the northern Tenasserim Range in Thailand and Burma comes the most beautiful member of the genus. The flowers, slightly over 1 inch across, appear from January to March on a short scape. The relatively thick sepals and petals are chartreuse with bold, deep-purple spots. The midlobe is slightly over $\frac{1}{2}$ inch across, hairy, and white with purple spots and a deep-yellow center. The leaves are 8 inches long and 1 inch wide.

Gastrochilus hybrids

Gastrochilus, a relatively little known group of orchids, has not figured in any hybridization program as yet. However, the attractive, long-lasting flowers of these species may warrant attempts at hybridizations. A cross between Gastr. bellinus and Gastr. dasypogon might combine the attractive floral characteristics of the former with the floriferousness and ease of culture of the latter. Also, some intergeneric hybridizations between Gastrochilus and Staurochilus or other sarcanthine orchids might yield novel and interesting types.

48

GRAMMATOPHYLLUM

The genus *Grammatophyllum* is known to be represented in Thailand by a single species, *Gram. speciosum*, which has the distinction of being not only the largest member of its group but perhaps the largest of the entire orchid family. The genus is allied to *Cymbidium* and consists of about six species from the Malaysian, Philippine and New Guinea areas.

Grammatophyllum speciosum Bl.

The canelike pseudobulbs are about 2 inches thick and 6 to 8 feet high. The leaves are about 20 inches long and 2 inches wide, tapered and curved downward toward the tip. The inflorescence originates from the base of the stem and rises to the height of the stem, carrying numerous flowers that are spaced more densely toward the tip. The individual flowers, about 4 inches across, are greenish yellow blotched with purplish brown. Some of the lower flowers may be abnormal, lacking in petal, sepal, labellum or column. Often the abnormal flower has two petals, two sepals and no lip. The flowering season is usually from July to October.

This species is commonly seen in the Chumporn region, growing on the trunks of the palmyra palm often together with *Cymbidium finlaysonianum*. It is also found in peninsular and southeastern Thailand, as well as in Pitsanuloke and Loei in northern Thailand. Its geographical distribution extends from Thailand, Malaysia, Sumatra and New Guinea to the Philippines.

Because this orchid grows to a tremendous size, it is more convenient to place it in a permanent spot in the garden rather than in a container. Being an epiphyte by nature, it should be provided with adequate drainage. The base of the plant should be well above the ground level. This can be accomplished by piling stones, bricks or crushed rock, incorporating some organic compost and anchoring the plant in this heap without covering the pseudobulbs. In a sunny location it will flower more freely, although plants generally do not flower annually. A large clump with numerous pseudobulbs, each producing a long spray of long-lasting flowers, is a magnificent sight.

HABENARIA

The polymorphic *Habenaria*, one of the largest genera of terrestrial orchids, has worldwide distribution. The species are deciduous and tuberous-rooted. Flowers vary from small and inconspicuous to large and showy. Among the 35 or more species found in Thailand, a few are very handsome and worthy of cultivation. The completely deciduous habit and the long period of dormancy of the subterranean tubers are the unattractive features of growing these orchids.

Habenaria rhodocheila Hance

This orchid, with bright scarlet flowers, is probably the most attractive *Habenaria* of Thailand. The showy portion of the flower is the large, four-lobed lip which measures about 1¼ inches long and 1 inch wide. The green dorsal sepal is about ½ inch long and hooded, and the light-green lateral sepals are curled under the large midlobe. The petals are short, green, tinged with red, and adjoin the dorsal sepal. The brownish spur is about 1½ inches long. From September to November, up to 15 flowers are borne on a 3 – inch rachis.

The plant, terminated by the inflorescence, is about 8 inches tall. The leaves are about 6 by 2 inches, green, mottled with light green and sometimes suffused with brown.

The geographical distribution of this species extends from southern China through Indochina, Thailand and Burma to Penang in Malaysia. In Thailand it has been found in all phytogeographical regions except the eastern and western regions. It is usually found in partially shaded areas, growing on large boulders near streams. The plants from Penang have yellow flowers; those of Thailand are scarlet.

The leaves and stem gradually dry out after the plant has flowered, and the underground tubers remain dormant during the ensuing dry months. Then, with the advent of the rainy season in late May, vegetative growth begins, and the flowers appear in the fall.

The most critical part of the culture of habenarias is the resting period. During the period of dormancy, the plants should be left in a relatively shaded, dry spot and watered sparingly. Beginning in May, water may be increased. The plants should be fertilized occasionally during the period of active growth.

At present, plants are still plentiful in their native habitat, and collectors gather them annually during the flowering season to bring them to the Bangkok weekend market for sale. If you do not have the facilities or the patience to cultivate the plants, they can be purchased and planted during the flowering season. An attractively potted plant with buds about to flower will provide enjoyment for a month or more.

50

Habenaria columbae Ridl.

A fine contrast to the above scarlet-flowered *Hab. rhodocheila* is the white *Hab. columbae*. About 15 flowers, measuring approximately 1 inch across, are borne on the apical 3 inches of a single slender and erect axis. The dorsal sepal and petals are short and adjoined to form a hood. The lateral sepals are slightly over ½ inch long and relatively broad. The midlobe is about ¾ by ¼ inch, while the side lobes are short and narrow. The dark-green spur is about 1 inch long. The rosetted leaves, about 3 by 1½ inches, lie flat on the soil. The flowering season is from September to November.

This orchid, distributed in Thailand and probably in neighboring Laos, has been found in all phytogeographic regions of Thailand except the peninsular area. In Prachuab, it has been found in abundance in the shade of bamboo.

Habenaria medioflexa Turril

This attractive endemic orchid comes from relatively high elevations in the northern, northeastern, eastern and southeastern parts of Thailand. A distinctive feature is the deeply fringed side lobes. The plant is about 2 feet tall, with flowers borne on the apical 5 inches of the erect axis. The greenish-white flowers are about 2 inches across. The dorsal sepal is relatively broad, the lateral lobes are slightly narrower, while the petals are almost threadlike. The midlobe is ¾ inch long and very narrow. The side lobes are deeply fringed on the edge away from the midlobe. The spur is more than 4 inches long, white toward the base and green toward the tip. The flowering season is September and October.

This species appears to be difficult to cultivate in Bangkok. When it is brought down from the high elevations in Prachinburi, the flowers and leaves often turn black and degenerate. If the plants are started early instead of being uprooted during the flowering time, they might do better.

51

PAPHIOPEDILUM

Paphiopedilum is a genus of more than 50 species, distributed south of the Himalayas along the Indo-Malayan region through Indonesia and to the Philippines. Thailand is represented by nine or more species. The term *Cypripedium* or "Cyps," has been in common usage by horticulturists for this group of orchids, but since the *Cypripedium* genus comprises species of ladyslippers which inhabit the north temperate regions, less confusion will exist if the botanically accepted *Paphiopedilum* is universally adopted for the Asiatic ladyslippers.

The paphiopedilums are predominantly terrestrials, growing in decomposed organic matter or in an accumulation of debris in rock crevices or ledges. They are often associated with mosses or ferns at high elevations. A few species are epiphytic. Those species which inhabit mountain forests at high elevations where humidity is high and temperature cool are often difficult to cultivate and flower when brought down to the lowlands of the tropics. On the other hand, such species as *Paph. niveum* and *Paph. exul*, which are inhabitants of low elevations, are easier to grow. Because the time of flowering varies with the species, year-round blooms can be obtained by growing an assortment of them. Besides their beauty, the long life of individual flowers is an important horticultural attribute of this group of orchids.

Species of *Paphiopedilum* were classified by Pfitzer into three subgenera, but according to Holttum, this classification may not be the most natural one. The species of Thailand might be conveniently grouped as follows : 1) the brachypetalums comprised of *Paph. bellatulum, Paph. niveum, Paph. godefroyae* and *Paph. concolor*, all characterized by roundish flowers and mottled leaves, 2) *Paph. parishii*, having long twisted petals similar to *Paph. philippinense*, 3) *Paph. villosum* and *Paph. exul*, having solid green leaves and being closely allied to *Paph. insigne*, and 4) *Paph. callosum, Paph. barbatum* and *Paph. sukhakulii*, having mottled leaves, and chromosomes numbers different from those of the above species.

Paphiopedilum bellatulum (Rchb. f.) Pfitz.

The leaves of this species, as well as others belonging to the brachypetalum group, are attractively mottled. They are dark green, mottled with pale green on the upper surface, and flushed with varying degrees of purple underneath. The white flowers are spotted with dark maroon, measure about $2\frac{1}{2}$ inches across and are round and compact. The concave dorsal sepal is about $2\frac{3}{4}$ inches wide. Much natural variation exists in the shape of the flower and the number and size of spots. The flower stems are short and weak, often carrying one and, occasionally, two flowers. Plants usually flower in April and May.

This species inhabits the Chiangdao mountain and other areas in northern

52

Thailand at high elevations. Brought down to low elevations, such as Bangkok, plants do not thrive. It is one of the more difficult species to grow under tropical conditions.

Paphiopedilum concolor (Batem.) Pfitz.

Flowers of this orchid are slightly smaller than those of *Paph. bellatulum*, measuring about 2 inches across. Small purplish spots appear on a pale-yellow base. The round and concave dorsal sepal is about 1 ¼ inches long and wide, and the petals are slightly longer and narrower. The pouch is about ½ inch wide and 1 ¼ inches long. The staminode is yellow, spotted with purple. The scape is about 4 inches long and carries up to three flowers. Peak flowering occurs in May, but flowers can be seen throughout the year. The mottled leaves are about 6 inches long and 1 ¾ inches wide.

Paph. concolor is found in the eastern, central, southeastern, southwestern and peninsular districts of Thailand. It is also distributed in neighboring Burma and Indochina. It is relatively easy to cultivate at low elevations and flowers rather freely. A potting mixture of coral or sand, leaf mold or peat, and fern fiber will give satisfactory results.

Paphiopedilum niveum (Rchb. f.) Pfitz.

The attractive white flowers of this species are dotted with many minute purple spots which are most numerous near the base of the sepals and petals and the infolded lobes of the labellum. Occasionally, pure-white forms are encountered. The flowers measure about 2 ½ inches across. The dorsal sepal is about 1 inch long and 1 ¼ inches wide, and the petals are about 1 ¼ inches long and much narrower. The staminode is lemon-yellow. One or two flowers are borne on relatively long, erect scapes, 7 inches or more high. Peak flowering in Thailand occurs in April or May, but flowers can be seen from December to August. The leaves, which are about 4 inches long and 1 ¼ inches wide, are dark green, mottled with light green on the upper surfaces and dark purple on the lower surfaces.

This orchid is found in the Langkawi area in northern Malaysia close to the Thailand border, and also in peninsular Thailand. It is found growing in rock crevices or ledges with accumulated debris on limestone hills which often extend down to the sea. The bulk of those growing naturally on Langkawi Island are said to have been removed through indiscriminate collecting. Collectors in Thailand, having somewhat depleted the supply in the border region, have advanced northward to the vicinity of Trang and Krabi. The northernmost limit of distribution in Thailand has not been established, but probably the habitat does not extend much farther north than Trang and Krabi, and the time when *Paph. niveum* becomes relegated to the "difficult to collect" species is not far away.

With its natural habitat at relatively low elevations in peninsular Thailand, it stands to reason that it can be successfully cultivated and flowered in typical tropical settings. This has been confirmed in Bangkok. A mixture of limestone, coral or sand, and leaf mold has given excellent results.

A natural variation of the typical *Paph. niveum* described above is "Ang Thong,"

53

which is found on Ang Thong and Samui Islands in Surasdhani in peninsular Thailand. Plant characteristics are highly variable, but generally the flowers are larger, and the purple spots appearing on a white background are more conspicuous than those of the type species. Since *Paph. niveum* and *Paph. godefroyae* occupy similar habitats, the possibility of a hybrid origin of "Ang Thong" cannot be discounted.

Paphiopedilum godefroyae (Godefr.) Pfitz.

Flowers are 3 inches across with many purple spots of variable size, some of which are fused, appearing on a creamish-yellow base. The petals are about $1\frac{3}{4}$ inches long and $1\frac{1}{4}$ inches wide, and the dorsal sepal is about $1\frac{1}{2}$ inches long and $1\frac{1}{4}$ inches wide. The staminode is stippled with minute purple spots. The flower stem is relatively short and bears one or two flowers from December to July. Leaves are about 4 inches long and 1 inch wide, mottled with light green on the upper surfaces and flushed with purple on the lower surfaces.

The habitat of this species is similar to that of *Paph. niveum*, and frequently both species have been collected from the same locality.

Paphiopedilum parishii (Rchb. f.) Pfitz.

Unlike most of the terrestrial or lithophytic species of *Paphiopedilum*, *Paph. parishii*, is epiphytic. It is found at high elevations in deciduous forests of the Khanburi region in western Thailand, as well as in neighboring Burma. It is quite distinct from the other Thailand *Paphiopedilum* species because of its long and twisted petals.

Flowers measure about 3 inches across and $4\frac{1}{4}$ inches long. The petals, which are about $3\frac{1}{4}$ inches long and $\frac{1}{2}$ inch wide, are greenish yellow with dark-purple spots near the base and solid purple toward the tip. Warts and hair are present on the lower margin. The dorsal sepal is $1\frac{1}{2}$ inches long and $\frac{3}{4}$ inch wide and is chartreuse striped with green. The purplish-green pouch is $\frac{3}{4}$ inch across. The staminode is white with a green center. The solid green leaves are 15 inches long and $1\frac{1}{2}$ inches wide. It normally flowers around June and July.

Paphiopedilum exul (O'Brien) Pfitz.

Leaves of this species are uniformly green, long and narrow, and measure about 10 inches long and $\frac{3}{4}$ inch wide. Flowers are 2 inches across and $2\frac{1}{2}$ inches long. The narrow, curved petals, $1\frac{3}{4}$ inches long and $\frac{1}{2}$ inch wide, are brownish yellow with a brown midrib. Hair is found toward the base. The white-margined, yellow-green dorsal sepal is spotted with purple and is $1\frac{3}{4}$ inches long and 1 inch wide. The pouch is brownish purple. The scape is relatively long and bears a single flower, usually from February to May. The native habitat of this species is from the rock crevices in the Chumporn region down to Krabi in southern Thailand. Not a difficult plant to grow and flower, it can be given similar treatment as *Paph. niveum*.

Paphiopedilum villosum (Ldl.) Pfitz.

The large, glossy flowers of this species measure 3 inches across and 3 $\frac{1}{2}$ inches long. The dorsal sepal, 2 inches long and 1 inch wide, is purple with a green tip. The petals are about 2 inches long and 1 inch wide, with a dark-purple midrib, purple toward the tip, and light lavender toward the base. The light-purple pouch is 1 inch wide. The staminode is white. Usually a single flower is carried on a 6 - inch flower stem during winter. Leaves are about 15 inches long and 1 $\frac{1}{2}$ inches wide and are solid green with purple spots near the base.

This epiphytic species is found at high elevations in the Chiengmai region, as well as in Burma and Assam. It is difficult to grow at low elevations.

Paphiopedilum callosum (Rchb. f.) Pfitz.

This handsome, large-flowered species comes from the mountain regions of Chiengmai and eastern Prachinburi. Flowers are about 3 $\frac{1}{4}$ inches across. The large, attractive, dorsal sepal is 1 $\frac{3}{4}$ inches long and 2 $\frac{1}{4}$ inches wide, with sides often curved back. It is white with alternating long and short veins changing from green at the base to purple toward the tip. The slightly S-shaped petals are 2 $\frac{1}{2}$ inches long and $\frac{1}{2}$ inch wide, green toward the base, purple toward the tip, and have dark-purple warts on the upper margin, accompanied by black hair. The lip is green, suffused with brownish purple. The green staminode is tinged with purple. The relatively long scape usually carries a solitary flower in April and May. The mottled leaves are about 9 inches long and 1 $\frac{3}{4}$ inches wide.

Paphiopedilum barbatum (Ldl.) Pfitz.

The flowers of this species are slightly smaller but similar to those of *Paph. callosum*. The dorsal sepal is nearly round, white toward the tip, green at the base and striped with purple at the center. The petals are straight instead of S-shaped, greenish toward the base, purplish toward the apex, with prominent hair on black warts on the upper margins. The pouch is brownish purple. The staminode is green with purple markings. Leaves are mottled.

Paph. barbatum has been found in Krabi, Songkla, Ranong and Phang-nga in peninsular Thailand. It is also distributed in the Malayan mountains at elevations between 2000 and 4000 feet, where it grows among sphagnum moss or in soil composed largely of decayed organic matter in moist yet well-drained areas.

Although *Paph. callosum* and *Paph. barbatum* are similar and at times difficult to distinguish, there are several characteristic morphological features such as the difference in shape of the petals and dorsal sepals. Also cytologically, they can be readily separated, for *Paph. callosum* has 32 chromosomes, while *Paph. barbatum* has 38. The closely related *Paph. sukhakulii* has 2n = 40 chromosomes. All other Thailand species of Paphiopedilum discussed earlier have 26 chromosomes, which is a common number for Paphiopedilum species.

Paphiodedilum sukhakulii Schoser & Senghas

This orchid was described and given the new species name, *Paph. sukhakulii*, by Schoser and Senghas in 1965. It comes from the Phu Luang Mountain in Loei Province in northeast Thailand. *Paph. callosum* also comes from the same region and is often mistaken for *Paph. sukhakulii* due to their similar vegetative characteristics and overlapping geographic distribution. *Paph. sukhakulii* is found in mountain flats close to the summit and along the banks of streams in sandy-loam soil richly mixed with decaying organic matter.

The narrow elliptic leaves are about 10 inches long and 2 inches wide. The leaves are mottled. The undersides of leaves do not have the purple spots of *Paph. callosum*. The leaf surface is somewhat rough in contrast to the smooth surface of *Paph. callosum*. The scape is brownish purple, hairy, about 10 inches long and usually bears a single flower, measuring about 3½ inches across. The 2 - by ¾ - inch petals are spread out horizontally. Numerous purplish brown spots occur on a light-green base. Hair is found on both upper and lower edges. The dorsal sepal is 1¼ inches long and 1 inch wide, broadly oval and tapered. It is white, striped with green. The ventral sepal is similar in color pattern but slightly shorter and narrower. The pouch is purplish brown.

Paphiopedilum hybrids

The first *Paphiopedilum* hybrid, *Paph. barbatum* X *Paph. villosum*, was registered in 1869. Since that time innumerable hybrids have appeared. *Sanders' List of Orchid Hybrids* enumerates more than 4000 *Paphiopedilum* hybrids up to 1946. From 1946 to 1963, approximately 1700 additional hybrids were produced, which indicates that this group of orchids has received continued attention from orchid hybridists.

Many of the round and compact modern hybrids represent considerably advanced generations from the original cross. According to Mrs. Sherman Adams, the pedigree of the modern hybrid, *Paph.* Clementine Churchill, involved 77 crosses. The species that are common to Thailand have contributed much in the development of modern hybrids. *Paph. villosum* has produced 66 hybrids ; *Paph. bellatulum* and *Paph. niveum*, 59 each ; *Paph. callosum*, 58 ; and *Paph. barbatum*, 50. *Paph. godefroyae*, *Paph. concolor* and *Paph. exul* have produced fewer hybrids, 31, 27 and 22, respectively, while *Paph. parishii* has figured in only 6 crosses.

Low fertility or complete sterility has been a common feature with *Paphiopedilum* hybrids, although some interspecific hybrids have been fertile and have given rise to additional hybrids. The low fertility of species hybrids is partly due to unequal chromosome numbers of the parental species. Many species have 26 chromosomes but others have 28 to 42 chromosomes. The outstanding primary hybrid, *Paph.* Maudiae, resulted from crossing *Paph. callosum* var. *sanderae*, with 32 chromosomes, and *Paph. lawrenceanum* var. *hyeanum*, with 36 chromosomes. *Paph.* Maudiae has 34 chromosomes, the intermediate number, and is low in fertility.

As in other groups of intensively hybridized orchids, polyploidy has played a major role in the production of the outstanding *Paphiopedilum* hybrids. Also, aneuploidy is not uncommon within this group because of the wide variation of chromosome numbers at the species level.

PHAIUS

Several large and handsome terrestrial species are included in the genus *Phaius*. Thailand is represented by four species of which *Phaius tankervilliae* is the most common and popular.

Phaius tankervilliae (Ait.) Bl.

This majestic orchid is also known as *Phaius grandifolius* as well as the Nun's Orchid in the vernacular. It is widely distributed from India, Burma, Thailand, Indochina, China and Malaysia to Australia and the Pacific, and has become naturalized in Hawaii and Jamaica. In Thailand it is found at relatively high elevations in northern, northeastern and eastern regions.

The clustered pseudobulbs are short, thick and green, with long leaves which measure about 3 feet. The inflorescence arises from the base of the pseudobulb to a length of about 4 feet and produces from 10 to 20 flowers, usually during March and April. Individual flowers are about 4 inches across. The sepals and petals are relatively narrow, white in the back and reddish brown in the front. The tubular lip is rose-purple inside and whitish outside.

This orchid generally inhabits the high elevations of Thailand and will not flower freely when brought down to Bangkok. However, because of its wide geographical distribution, it should be possible to obtain races that are adapted to varied environmental conditions.

The potting mixture should consist of well-aerated soil and organic compost. Plants should be grown in light shade, watered liberally during the growing season and fertilized frequently. They will grow and flower best in relatively cool climates and can tolerate a temperature as low as 40° F.

Phaius hybrids

Phaius tankervilliae, as well as other related species, have been under cultivation in England since the latter part of the nineteenth century. Many hybrids were produced among the species and between *Phaius* and *Calanthe*. A review of the awards given by the Royal Horticultural Society of England reflects the popularity and intensity of culture and hybridization in the past. Around the turn of the century, 30 *Phaius* and 11 *Phaiocalanthe* hybrids received the Award of Merit or the First Class Certificate.

An intergeneric hybrid between *Phaius tankervilliae* and *Cymbidium giganteum* was registered as *Phaiocymbidium* Chardwarense by Moore in 1902.

PHALAENOPSIS

Phalaenopsis is a fairly large genus of approximately 70 known species, widely distributed from the Himalayas through Malaysia, Indonesia, New Guinea, Australia and the Philippines to Formosa. Most of the fine species of this group come from the Philippines and neighboring areas, and only two relatively insignificant species are known to occur within Thailand.

Phalaenopsis cornu-cervi (Breda) Bl. & Rchb. f.

The inflorescence of this species is branched and characteristically flattened, with conspicuous alternating bracts. Only a few flowers are open at any time, but production of flowers usually continues for several months, and flowers can be seen throughout the year, although more plentifully during the rainy season. Individual flowers, which generally last for 2 weeks, measure about 1 ¼ inches wide and 1 ½ inches long. The sepals and petals are greenish yellow, spotted and barred with brown, and are narrow and pointed, forming a relatively open-type flower. The leaves are fleshy and measure about 6 inches long and 2 inches wide.

This orchid is known to exist in Burma, Thailand, Malaysia and Indonesia. It is a relatively common species, widely distributed within Thailand. It extends from the Chiengmai region in the north down to Khanburi in the western region and to the peninsular region, and from eastern Prachinburi to southeastern Chandhaburi. Such widely occurring species usually have a great range of adaptability. It does well attached to pieces of tree fern, staghorn fern or coconut husk, or potted in fern fiber or a mixture of fern fiber and charcoal.

Phalaenopsis decumbens (Griff.) Holtt.

This diminutive *Phalaenopsis* species was also designated as *Kingiella decumbens* Rolfe. According to Holttum, the separation of this species into the genus *Kingiella* is not warranted. The flowers measure only ¾ inch across. The petals and sepals are of about equal dimensions and are relatively broad, forming a flat, well-proportioned flower. The petals and sepals are white with minute spots of purple toward the base. The deeply cleft, white-tipped midlobe, as well as the side lobes, are dark purple – an attractive contrast to the rest of the flower. Both midlobe and side lobes have toothlike appendages near the base. The branching inflorescence is about 10 inches long, bearing several flowers over a period of 3 to 4 months, usually beginning in May. Frequently, two flowers open at a time, and individual flowers last about 2 weeks. The leaves are about 3 ½ by 2 inches, flat, broad and thin, and often have wavy margins.

Holttum states that *Phal. decumbens* is the most widely distributed species of

Phalaenopsis. It occurs in South India, Ceylon, Burma, Thailand, Cambodia, Viet Nam, Malaysia, Indonesia and the Philippines. In Thailand it is found from eastern Nakornnayok to southeastern Chandhaburi, and from western Khanburi to peninsular Thailand. The easiest method of culture is to attach the plants to tree fern slabs and provide a relatively heavy shade.

Phalaenopsis hybrids

A few hybrids of *Phal. cornu-cervi* have appeared, but none has proven outstanding. Apparently the yellow color of *Phal. cornu-cervi* is not transmitted to its immediate offspring.

Probably due to the diminutive size of flowers and partly to the unavailability in growers' collections, *Phal. decumbens* has been ignored as parental material. If miniature phalaenopsis orchids are desired, then *Phal. decumbens* might play an important role in hybridization.

RENANTHERA

Renanthera is generally known for the spectacular red-blossomed sprays of some of its species, and the transmission of certain desirable characteristics to their offspring. A relatively small genus of approximately 10 species, it is distributed from the Himalayas and South China through Indochina, Thailand, Burma, Malaysia, Indonesia and New Guinea to the Philippines. *Renanthera* is represented in Thailand by *Ren. coccinea, Ren. isosepala* and *Ren. histrionica*.

Renantheras are relatively easy to cultivate. Cuttings can be placed in a raised bed filled with tree fern chunks or fibers, coconut husks or other media, and appropriately staked. If it is desirable to move flowering plants for decorative purposes, a tree-fern stump or totem pole can be placed in the center of a large pot and the plants attached to the pole. Plants and pole can be secured firmly by filling the pot with tree-fern fiber, charcoal, gravel, etc. When the plants are established, they should be grown under full exposure to sun for best flowering.

Renanthera coccinea Lour.

This orchid is similar in general characteristics to the Philippine *Ren. storiei,* except for its slightly brighter red blossoms. The horizontally arranged, branched inflorescence produces more than 75 bright-red flowers in a spectacular display, usually from March to May. Individual flowers are $1\frac{1}{2}$ by $2\frac{1}{2}$ inches. The narrow petals and dorsal sepals are orange-red, mottled with dark red. The lateral sepals are darker red (currant red), narrow at the base, but broadened to about $\frac{1}{4}$ inch, with the adjacent undulating margins often touching. The dark-red midlobe has a white blotch at the base, while the side lobes are yellow, striped with deep red. The upright stems attain a height of 15 feet or more. Leaves are light green, unequally bilobed, leathery and measure about 4 by $1\frac{1}{2}$ inches.

Native also to South China and Indochina, *Ren. coccinea* is generally found in eastern Thailand and neighboring Cambodia. Because cytological examination of *Ren. coccinea* cultivated in Hawaii revealed the hexaploid nature, it was assumed that the species is hexaploid. Subsequent examination of *Ren. coccinea* plants collected from the native habitats of Thailand disclosed the diploid number of $2n = 38$. The plants cultivated in Hawaii were originally introduced from Singapore. It is quite possible that the hexaploids originated as horticultural variants rather than as a naturally occurring hexaploid race.

Renanthera isosepala Holtt.

In 1964 we collected, from the scrub forest in Prachuab, flowering specimens

61

of *Renanthera* which, from a distance, appeared to be *Ren. coccinea*. On closer examination, however, it was discovered that the flowers were smaller than those of *Ren. coccinea* and the shape and size of the flower parts differed. Subsequently, we sent specimens to Dr. Holttum at Kew for identification. He concluded that this was a new species and gave it the name *Ren. isosepala.*

The inflorescence, which is about 16 inches long, consists of three or four lateral branches carrying up to 30 flowers. The natural spread of individual flowers is 7/8 inch by 1 3/8 inches. The petals and dorsal sepals are relatively short, very narrow, and measure about ½ by 1/8 inch. Lateral sepals are equal in length to the dorsal sepal, but twice as wide from about midpoint, and sharply diverge to form an angle of almost 90 degrees. Sepals and petals are uniformly orange-red with deep-red spots toward the base. The deep-orange-red midlobe is curved under. The side lobe is also orange-red toward the tip, with two white calli at the base. The spur is dark red and somewhat laterally compressed. The thick, leathery, unequally bilobed leaves are about 3½ inches long and 1 inch wide. The stems are about ¼ inch thick with an internode of about 1 inch.

The general plant characteristics of this orchid are similar to those of *Ren. coccinea*, and, except for the slightly smaller size, it is often difficult to distinguish between the two on the basis of vegetative characteristics. However, the flower size and form are distinctive. This species flowers from July to September, while *Ren. coccinea* flowers from March to May.

Renanthera histrionica Rchb. f.

Although *Ren. histrionica* is not a very showy species compared to the other *Renanthera* species, it is still worthy of cultivation because of its unique flowers. The inflorescence is short and bears about six flowers, with one or two flowers open at a time. The inverted flowers measure about 1 inch across. Petals and sepals are yellow, spotted with crimson along the edges and tips. The petals are curved away from the dorsal sepal, while the lateral sepals are curved back and are often touching each other. The long curved column is spotted with red. The leaves are curved, fleshy, channeled and gradually tapered to a point. The stems are climbing and hanging. It flowers freely throughout the year.

This orchid is unlike the other *Renanthera* species in general plant and flowering habit. Ridley, on the basis of the long column, inverted flowers and pointed leaves, placed it in a new genus, *Renantherella*. It is apparently an uncommon species in Thailand, for the only record of its occurrence is in Songkla in peninsular Thailand near the Malaysian border.

Renanthera hybrids

Outstanding intrageneric and intergeneric hybrids of *Renanthera* have arisen from the Philippine *Ren. storiei*, perhaps the finest member of the group. Excellent hybrids have resulted among *Aranthera* (*Arachnis* X *Renanthera*), *Renantanda* (*Renanthera* X *Vanda*), *Renanopsis* (*Renanthera* X *Vandopsis*), and *Renanstylis* (*Renanthera* X *Rhynchostylis*). Similar intergeneric hybrids have been made with *Ren. coccinea*, but results have not equaled those with *Ren. storiei*. Other intergeneric hybrids of *Renanthera* which have appeared more recently are *Renades* (*Renanthera* X *Aerides*), *Renaglottis* (*Renanthera* X *Trichoglottis*) and *Renancentrum* (*Renanthera* X *Ascocentrum*).

Many of the intergeneric hybrids are low in fertility due to the poor pairing between parental chromosomes at meiosis. If balanced tetraploid or amphidiploid hybrids having two sets of chromosomes each of the parental species are obtained, complete fertility can be restored and multiple species combinations can be readily effected. Crossing hexaploid and diploid plants of *Ren. coccinea* should result in tetraploid *Ren. coccinea*. The tetraploids, in turn, might be crossed with tetraploid plants of other species, such as *Vanda denisoniana* and *Aerides odorata*, to produce fertile amphidiploids which, subsequently, can be crossed with different species and hybrids to produce multiple genome combinations.

RHYNCHOSTYLIS

Rhynchostylis is a relatively small genus represented in Thailand by three excellent species, *Rhy. gigantea, Rhy. retusa* and *Rhy. coelestis*. This group of orchids has gained considerable popularity in recent years, particularly due to the appearance of color variations in the trade and to the production of some highly desirable intergeneric hybrids.

There has been much confusion over the years about the nomenclature of this group. For example, *Rhy. gigantea* was also designated as *Saccolabium giganteum, Vanda densiflora, Saccolabium densiflorum* and *Rhynchostylis densiflora*. Until a few years ago the name *Saccolabium giganteum* prevailed, but now *Rhy. gigantea* is generally accepted and used in the registration of orchid hybrids.

Both *Rhy. gigantea* and *Rhy. retusa* are relatively easy to cultivate and flower in the lowlands, and lend themselves to the production of specimen plants with spectacular displays of densely arranged, attractive inflorescences. *Rhy. coelestis* may not be as free-flowering at low elevations, although plants from southern Thailand can be expected to behave favorably. Plants can be grown in pots or baskets without any medium, or with charcoal or coarse tree-fern fiber. They require good aeration and drainage and a shade of about 50 to 60 percent. All of these species do well attached to tree trunks or branches.

Rhynchostylis gigantea (Ldl.) Ridl.

This species is widely distributed in Thailand from the eastern areas around Prachinburi on northward through Nakorn Sawan and Loei to Chiengmai and down to western Khanburi. The flowers are white, with amethyst-purple spots of variable size and density. The arched or drooping flower spikes are 8 to 12 inches long, carrying about 50 flowers, each measuring 1 to 1½ inches. A medium-sized plant often produces three or four flower spikes, and a large plant may produce seven or more spikes during a single flowering season. In Bangkok, a large many-branched specimen produced as many as 30 flower spikes. The fleshy leaves measure from 10 to 12 inches in length and 2 to 3 inches in width, are unequally lobed at the tip, and are characteristically variegated with light and dark green.

Flower spikes are usually initiated in early September but remain dormant until the advent of the cool season, when they begin to elongate and develop flower buds. Flowers often appear from mid-January through February, and individual flowers last about 2 weeks.

Besides the wide natural variation in size and density of spots of the common type, there are two additional distinct color variations – red, or amethyst-purple, and white. The red form, "Chang Daeng" (red elephant), has been known in Thailand for more than 60 years. However, among the thousands of plants of *Rhy. gigantea* collected from the wilds, only about eight have turned out to be red, thus reflecting the scarcity of this color mutation. The leaves of this variant are purplish red and can be distinguished easily from the common and white types which do not have this anthocyanin color.

In 1954, Sagarik successfully crossed two red clones which resulted in the greatly increased availability of plants with red flowers. About 80 percent of the progeny were red, while the rest were the common type, which indicated that red is a dominant character. This color is affected by temperatures preceding the flowering period. When the winter temperatures are relatively high, the amethyst-purple coloration does not develop fully, and many plants produce flowers with large white blotches.

The white form, although not as rare in nature as the red, is nevertheless relatively uncommon in growers' collections. Several crosses involving superior white types have been made, which should result in an increased number of improved white.

Plants from the northern region of Chiengmai have heavier stems, shorter, thicker and darker green leaves, and larger flowers than those from other regions. Although these characteristics suggest a polyploid condition, chromosome number determination has shown 2n = 38, which is the common number for all species of *Rhynchostylis*.

Rhynchostylis retusa Bl.

This handsome, easily grown orchid is often referred to as the Foxtail Orchid. Large plants are branched and generally similar in habit to *Rhy. gigantea*. The leaves are about 10 inches long and 1 inch wide, unequally toothed at the tip and striated with light green. Individual flowers are relatively small, measuring from ½ to ¾ inch across. The sepals and petals are white with numerous minute purple spots, and the fleshy labellum is flushed with purple. Pure white forms, which are rarely encountered in the wilds, have been collected from Nakorn Sawan and Tak in northwest Thailand. Flower spikes, reaching 16 inches in length, carry as many as 140 flowers, densely arranged to form an attractive cylindrical, drooping spray. Like *Rhy. gigantea*, a medium-sized plant usually produces three or four inflorescences. A large specimen plant with 5 branches produced 27 long, beautiful sprays. The flowering season is from April to May, and flowers generally last for 2 weeks.

Rhy. retusa has a wide geographical distribution. It is known to occur in Ceylon, India, Thailand, Indochina, Malaysia and the Philippines. In Thailand it is found in most of the phytogeographic regions, including peninsular Thailand. The plants found at high elevations in the Chiengmai mountains are large and have broad leaves, but are not free-flowering at low elevations.

Rhynchostylis coelestis Rchb. f.

The general characteristics of this handsome blue *Rhynchostylis* differ somewhat from those of the two species described above. The closely arranged conduplicate or tightly V-shaped leaves are recurved. The leaves measure about 9 inches long and $1\frac{1}{4}$ inches wide. The flower spikes are upright and carry 50 or more densely arranged, fragrant flowers. An individual flower measures from $\frac{1}{2}$ to $\frac{3}{4}$ inch across. The broad and often overlapping sepals and petals are light to purplish blue and slightly darker at the tips. The deeper colored labellum is often curved upward and covers the column. A few plants with pure-white flowers have been found in the northern part of Thailand. Peak flowering occurs during May, but flowering often begins in mid-April and extends to July. Individual flowers last about 2 weeks.

Plants are generally found in the deciduous forests of Thailand where the dry season is relatively long. They are widely distributed in the mountain areas in northern, northeastern, western and southwestern Thailand. However in the Prachuab area in southwestern Thailand, they are found at low elevations. In the city of Chiengmai, numerous plants can be seen growing on teak trees lining the streets. According to Seidenfaden and Smitinand, this orchid is endemic to Thailand.

Rhynchostylis hybrids

The first hybrid of *Rhynchostylis*, *V.* Miss Joaquim X *Rhy. gigantea*, was registered in 1958, but since then more than 50 hybrids have been registered with the three *Rhynchostylis* species, clearly reflecting the increased attention this group of orchids has been receiving. Intergeneric hybrids have been successfully produced with *Aerides, Arachnis, Ascocentrum, Neofinetia, Phalaenopsis, Renanthera, Vanda* and *Vandopsis*. About half of the total number of hybrids have been *Rhynchovanda*. Outstanding among the earlier hybrids is *Renanstylis* Queen Emma (*Ren. storiei* X *Rhy. gigantea*), several plants of which have received recognition for horticultural excellence. *Rhynchovanda* Blue Angel (*V.* Rothschildiana X *Rhy. coelestis*) and *Rhynchorides* Springtime (*Aer. lawrenceae* X *Rhy. gigantea*) have proven to be highly desirable hybrids. In addition to the intergeneric hybrids, a few multigeneric hybrids involving *Rhynchostylis* species have appeared.

Rhy. retusa has produced only 4 intergeneric hybrids to date, whereas the other species have produced about 25 hybrids each. *Rhy. coelestis* transmits the blue color to its offspring.

The intergeneric and multigeneric hybrids involving *Rhynchostylis* species have provided numerous novel and attractive vandaceous orchid hybrids.

SPATHOGLOTTIS

Spathoglottis is a genus of approximately 40 terrestrial orchids, widely distributed in Southeast Asia and the Pacific region extending to New Caledonia and Samoa. Many species have bright, beautiful, medium-sized flowers on tall, erect spikes, which make them worthy subjects for cultivation. Several species, and particularly the much improved hybrids, have been used in some gardens of the tropics.

Five species are known to occur in Thailand. Of these, the widespread *Spa. plicata* and *Spa. lobbii* are commonly encountered.

Spathoglottis plicata Bl.

This extremely variable species is native to India, Thailand, Malaysia, Indonesia and the Philippines. It generally inhabits the grassy lowlands and is common in the peninsular region of Thailand. The ovoid pseudobulbs are clustered. The leaves, up to $2\frac{1}{2}$ feet long and 3 inches wide, are pleated or folded. The scape is about 2 feet long and bears up to 40 flowers successively over a considerable length of time, with 5 or 6 flowers open at a time. Flowers are $1\frac{1}{2}$ inches across, with colors ranging from dark purple to lighter shades of purple to white. At the base of the midlobe are two bright-yellow calli.

The cultivated varieties of *Spa. plicata*, many of which have been named, are generally much improved in size, form and color over their counterparts growing in their native habitats.

Spa. plicata is easy to cultivate in the garden. For the best results the soil should be porous, well drained and free from encroaching tree roots. Organic compost or barnyard manure should be worked into the soil before planting. After the plants are well established, an occasional application of a chemical fertilizer will allow them to retain their vigor and floriferousness. Plants will flower throughout the year, although more abundantly during the dry period.

For pot culture, the same type of soil mixture as indicated above should be satisfactory. The bottom half of the pot should be filled with broken pieces of crockery, crushed brick or gravel, to insure adequate drainage. In planting, only the lower portion of the pseudobulbs should be covered with soil. The plants should receive liberal amounts of water and sunlight.

Spathoglottis lobbii Rchb. f.

The attractive golden-yellow *Spa. lobbii* is found in northeastern, eastern and southeastern Thailand. The pseudobulbs are flattened and somewhat triangular and remain dormant without leaves during the dry season. The narrow leaves, 14 inches

67

by ¾ inch, are produced during the rainy season. The inflorescence appears a few months later. The scape is about 2 feet long, slender, erect, and bears successively up to 25 flowers. The flowering season usually extends from September through November. The cobalt-yellow flowers are about 1 ¼ inches across. The dorsal sepal and petals are of about equal size, and the lateral sepals are slightly wider, with a few brownish streaks confined to the basal area. At the base of the midlobe are two relatively tall calli, spotted with reddish brown. The side lobes are somewhat rectangular with streaks and minute spots toward the base.

This orchid is also native to Indochina and Burma. It is similar to and perhaps identical to *Spa. affinis*, described in *Flora of Malaya*.

Because it inhabits high elevations, *Spa. lobbii* is not easy to grow when brought down to low elevations. If given proper care, however, it may possibly be cultivated in the lowlands. After flowering, plants should be maintained in a sheltered, ventilated spot with restricted watering.

In about 4 months, the pseudobulbs should be lifted out, divided if necessary, and planted in a well-aerated, well-drained soil mixed with organic compost. The pseudobulbs should be covered with a thin layer of soil and kept in a sheltered spot until about May, when growth begins. During the period of leaf growth, plants should be watered daily and fertilized occasionally.

Spathoglottis hybrids

Over the years, several *Spathoglottis* hybrids have appeared, particularly through the efforts of orchidists in Singapore and Hawaii. *Spa. plicata* has figured in about a dozen hybrids, and *Spa. lobbii* and *Spa. affinis* have produced three hybrids. In Thailand, hybridization with this group has resulted in superior forms. Unfortunately, the identity of the parents of some of the crosses has not been retained.

Although species of *Spathoglottis* interbreed freely, the hybrids are usually of low fertility. This has hindered the recombination of characters in the second and later generations. The use of green-pod culture should circumvent part of the sterility barrier in the primary hybrids.

TRICHOGLOTTIS (STAUROCHILUS)

Seidenfaden and Smitinand, in *The Orchids of Thailand*, placed *Trichoglottis fasciata* and *Trichoglottis dawsoniana* in the genus *Staurochilus*. Holttum, in *Flora of Malaya*, kept *Trgl. fasciata* in the genus *Trichoglottis*. Since several bigeneric and trigeneric hybrids of *Trgl. fasciata* have already been registered, it may be desirable to retain the genus name *Trichoglottis*.

Trichoglottis is a genus of 30 or more species. Eight species have been recorded for Thailand. Only two of these, *Trgl. fasciata* and *Trgl. dawsoniana*, which have been separated into the *Staurochilus* genus by Seidenfaden and Smitinand, can be considered to be of horticultural interest.

Trichoglottis fasciata Rchb. f.

This orchid is distributed in Indochina, Thailand, North Malaysia, Sumatra and the Philippines. In Thailand, it is a common species found in practically every phytogeographic region. The erect stems are ½ inch in diameter, with unequally bilobed leaves about 5 inches long and 1 inch wide, and attain a height of over 5 feet. Usually around April and May, two to four flowers open on slightly ascending, relatively short scapes. The flowers measure about 2 inches across. The front of the sepals and petals is yellow, with bold transverse brown bands, and the back is white. The lip is spotted sparsely with brown. The two lateral lobes of the midlobe are triangular and flattened horizontally, and the front end of the midlobe is flattened vertically with a pointed tip. The side lobes are erect and close to each other. The brown column has horns with yellow tips.

Trgl. fasciata can be cultivated in the same way as *Renanthera coccinea*. For best flowering, it should receive full sunlight at least part of the day. Several plants, attached to a tree-fern log or a comparable support and placed in a pot, produce an attractive display when in full bloom.

Trichoglottis dawsoniana Rchb. f.

Although much smaller in habit and size of flower than the species described above, *Trgl. dawsoniana* is quite attractive, with more numerous flowers on a branching inflorescence about 18 inches long. The lateral branches are about 4 inches long, each of which bears about eight 1 - inch flowers, usually in April and May. Sepals and petals of about equal dimensions have brown transverse blotches on a pale yellow base. The back is light chartreuse with white toward the base. The midlobe is golden yellow. The lateral lobes of the three-lobed midlobe are narrow, and the apical midlobe has a cleft. The brownish yellow side lobes are erect, narrow and tapered. The anther cap and column are brownish yellow. Stems are erect, about 2 feet tall, and bear leaves that are about 5 inches long and 1 inch wide.

This species appears to be endemic to Thailand. It is found in the Tenasserim Mountains in northern Thailand. Plants grow best when attached to a short support and planted in a pot filled with fern fiber or a mixture of fern fiber and charcoal.

Trichoglottis hybrids

In 1958, *Arachnoglottis* Brown Bars, a hybrid of *Trgl. fasciata* and *Arachnis* Maggie Oei, was registered by the Singapore Botanic Garden. Since then, two *Trichovanda*, three *Renaglottis* and two trigeneric hybrids have appeared, with *Trgl. fasciata* as one of the parents. None has proved to be especially outstanding. No hybrids of the second species, *Trgl. dawsoniana*, has appeared.

The Philippine species, *Trgl. brachiata*, has figured in the production of five *Trichovanda* hybrids, among which probably *Trichovanda* Ulaula (*Trgl. brachiata* X *V. sanderiana*) is the finest.

VANDA

Vanda species and hybrids have been very popular among hobbyists as well as commercial growers, particularly in the warmer areas of the world, including Thailand, Singapore, Hawaii and southern Florida. The genus *Vanda* comprises 30 to 40 species, distributed from the Himalayas through Southeast Asia to New Guinea and northern Australia. About 12 species occur in Thailand, including the highly esteemed "Queen of Vandas," *V. coerulea*. They can be classified into three groups on the basis of their leaves : 1) terete, 2) semiterete, or narrowly channelled, and 3) flat or strap. The first group is represented in Thailand by two species, *V. teres* and *V. hookeriana*. Only one species from the second group, *V. amesiana*, is known to occur in Thailand. The balance of the species fall into the flat or strap-leaf group.

The terete-leaved species can be propagated readily from cuttings 1 to 2 feet long. Cuttings can be planted in beds filled with coconut husks, tree fern, wood shavings, leaf mold or similar decaying organic matter and placed in direct sun. The plants will require wire or other support. Another method is to place cuttings around pieces of lumber, posts or tree-fern stumps. The posts should not be taller than 2 feet because the plants usually will not flower until the stems grow above the support. The plants should be fertilized and watered regularly.

The semiterete and strap vandas are commonly grown in wood baskets or clay pots hung with wires, or in pots placed on benches in shade houses. Tree fern or charcoal can be used as a medium. A more recent practice is to secure plants in pots or baskets with sticks or wires, but without any medium. Roots will soon become firmly attached to the container and eventually hang out. Plants should be fertilized with liquid fertilizer every 2 weeks.

Most of the species inhabiting high elevations in nature will not thrive when brought down to low elevations, and flowering is usually sparse. However, some of the plants grown from seeds appear to adapt better than plants collected from the wilds.

Vanda teres Ldl.

This species is widely distributed in Thailand at various elevations and in most of the phytogeographic regions. It is also found in neighboring Laos, Burma and the foothills of the Himalayas. In its native habitat it is found climbing on tree trunks or thickets, often forming branched, tangled masses several feet long. The stems are cylindrical, $\frac{1}{4}$ by 3/8 inch thick. Each internode is about 2 inches long and covered with a leaf sheath. The terete leaves are either erect or curved. The inflorescence is about 8 inches long, bearing two to five flowers from $2\frac{1}{2}$ to 3 inches across. The petals are twisted at the base up to 180 degrees, so that the abaxial surface appears as the front of the petal. The broad side lobes

71

fold over the column, and the midlobe has a deep cleft. The spur is pointed and about $\frac{3}{4}$ inch long. There is much variation in size and color in this species. The most common coloration of petals is mauve, with slightly lighter sepals and slightly darker lip. The throat of the lip is yellow. Flowers also may be darker or lighter colored, or white. Flowering usually is from April to July.

Vanda hookeriana Rchb. f.

   V. hookeriana is limited in its distribution in Thailand to the southern peninsular region, close to the Malaysian border. This species occurs in high rainfall, humid areas among low shrubs and thickets. It is also native to Malaysia, Sumatra and Borneo. The terete stems are thinner and weaker than those of *V. teres*. The leaves are light green and can be readily distinguished from those of *V. teres* by the constriction about 1 inch from the tip. The inflorescence bears several flowers about $2\frac{1}{2}$ inches across. The sepals and petals are white tinged with pale lavender. The petals are twisted at the base, similar to *V. teres*. The side lobes are spreading and dark purple, and the broad midlobe is light lavender with rich purple markings. The midlobe, unlike that of *V. teres*, is broad, three-lobed and without the deep cleft. The spur is very short.

Vanda amesiana Rchb. f.

   The only representative of the semiterete group in Thailand, this charming vanda has narrowly channelled leaves that are 10 inches long. The relatively small flowers measure from 1 to $1\frac{1}{2}$ inches across. Sepals and petals are white with a pink tinge. The broad midlobe is amethyst-purple. This species is found at high elevations in northern Thailand and Burma. It has been flowered under cultivation in Chiengmai in northern Thailand, but will not do as well at low elevations in the tropics.

Vanda coerulea Griff.

   This is by far the most popular *Vanda* species of Thailand. It is found at relatively high elevations of northern and western regions of Thailand, as well as in Burma and the Khasi Hills in India. Plants are usually attached to trees in open forests, well exposed to the sun. The climate in their natural habitats is cool and moist. Even during the summer months of Thailand, from March to May when the day temperatures rise to 95° to 100° F, the night temperatures drop to around 50° F.

   The strap leaves of this orchid are short and thick, often about 6 inches long and 1 inch wide. The tip is unequally notched. The long ascending inflorescence carries from 10 to 15 flowers, each measuring 3 to 4 inches across. There is much variation in color, from blue-tinted white to deep blue, and bluish lavender to pink. Also, the color of petals may be solid or beautifully tessellated. The petals are usually twisted at the base, exposing the back of the petals. However, improved forms without twisted petals are available. The dark-blue lip is small with narrow, curved side lobes. The spur is short. Flowers are obtained throughout the year, but usually the peak season is in August. Flowers often last for 3 weeks.

72

Plants are well suited for cultivation in Chiengmai, situated in northern Thailand at 19°N and 1023 feet elevation. Here, the night temperatures drop below 55° F, which promotes floral initiation and development. An annual orchid show, staged in August, features spectacular displays of this orchid. Selected plants, with round overlapping sepals and petals of good color and without the twisting of petals, have given rise to vastly improved forms.

Vanda denisoniana Bens. & Rchb. f.

Improved forms of this species are highly prized. This orchid is favored because of the white to clear-yellow flowers with excellent form and also for its delightful fragrance. The flowering season is from January to March. Color varies from ivory-white, chartreuse, lemon-yellow, golden-yellow, yellow-brown to copper. Flowers are about 2½ inches across, waxy and of heavy substance. Up to about eight flowers are borne close together on relatively short scapes. The apex of the midlobe is two-lobed. The leaves are 10 inches by 1 inch and recurved.

This orchid comes from several high elevation areas in northern and northeastern Thailand and neighboring Burma. It is a highly variable species. The type with sulfur-yellow flowers, marked with brown or copper bars or spots, has been given the botanical variety status, *hebraica* Rchb. f. This type was determined to be predominantly tetraploid $(2n = 76)$; the more prevalent type with white, green to yellow flowers was found to be diploid $(2n = 38)$.

Vanda coerulescens Griff.

The relatively small, lilac-colored flowers measure about 1¼ inches across. The scape is slender, long and erect, and carries from 12 to 20 flowers. The pedicel is about 2 inches long. The petals are slightly twisted at the base. The lip is dark mauve. This species has been reported to occur in Doi Sutep, south of Denchai and Mae Hawn Sawn in northern Thailand, and in Burma.

Vanda lilacina Teysmann & Binnend.

This delightful miniature *Vanda* species, also known as *V. laotica* Guill., is widely distributed in practically all phytogeographic regions except the Central Plains and peninsular Thailand. It also occurs in neighboring Laos and possibly Cambodia. The erect inflorescence bears as many as 20 flowers, each about ¾ inch across. The often overlapping sepals and petals are white with lavender tips. The side lobes are triangular, and the truncate midlobe broadens slightly at the tip and is rolled backward. The spur is broadly conical. The relatively short leaves measure up to 5 inches. This elegant miniature orchid is worthy of cultivation. It should be most useful in producing novel miniature vandaceous hybrids.

Vanda parviflora Ldl.

The individual flowers are slightly under 1 inch across. From 10 to 20 flowers

73

are carried on an erect inflorescence. The sepals and petals are pale yellow. The petals are twisted. The side lobes are small and obliquely triangular. The yellow midlobe is somewhat funnel-shaped, with keels ending toward the apex in two rounded calli. The spur is slender and curved forward. This species is native to Ceylon, India, Burma and Thailand. It has been collected from Doi Suthep and Mae Hawn Sawn in northern Thailand.

Vanda bensoni Batem.

This orchid produces several flowers, about 2 inches across, on relatively long flower spikes. The outer surfaces of the sepals and petals are light lavender, and the inner surfaces are brown with darker brown tessellation. The side lobes are white and narrower than those of *V. denisoniana*. The purple midlobe is narrow toward the base and expanded toward the tip into two lobes. The leaves are about 8 inches long. It flowers during March and April. This species is found in northern Thailand and neighboring Burma.

Vanda brunnea Rchb. f.

The rather open inflorescence is erect, 20 inches or longer, and carries a dozen or more flowers, usually around March and April. The flowers are small, measuring about $1\frac{1}{2}$ inches across when flower parts are flattened. The peduncles are slender and excessively long, about $2\frac{1}{4}$ inches. The petals are often reflexed. Petals and sepals are wavy-edged, and longer than wide. The outer surface is yellow to light brown, and the inner surface is brown to purplish brown, either nearly solid, slightly spotted or tessellated. The side lobes are triangular and brownish yellow. The basal part of the midlobe is narrow, long, and purple. The apical portion is expanded into two purplish brown lobes which may be rounded or truncated. The long, conically tapered spur is pale yellow. The column is purple. The recurved leaves are closely spaced, about 7 inches long and 1 inch wide. This species occurs in the northern, northeastern and western regions of Thailand and in Burma. The long scape of this orchid might be a desirable characteristic to be bred into hybrids for cut flowers.

Vanda hybrids

Vanda teres has been used in numerous crosses to date. An early hybrid, registered in 1893, is the widely cultivated *V.* Miss Joaquim (*V. teres* X *V. hookeriana*), a clone of which received the First Class Certificate from the Royal Horticultural Society. This hybrid is grown commercially in Hawaii for use in flower leis. Many crosses were made between *V. teres* and strap-leaf species and hybrids to produce semiterete hybrids. Two semiterete species hybrids, *V.* Emma van Deventer (*V. teres* X *V. tricolor*) and *V.* Josephine van Brero (*V. insignis* X *V. teres*), were the parents of the outstanding triploid hybrids, *V.* Nellie Morley and *V.* Tan Chay Yan, respectively. Semiterete species hybrids are usually low in fertility, due to the poor chromosome homology of terete and strap-leaf species. For both *V.* Emma van Deventer and *V.*

74

Josephine van Brero, highly fertile tetraploid or amphidiploid clones were used to produce the superior hybrids. The resulting triploid hybrids consist of one set of chromosomes, or genome, of *V. teres* and one genome each of two strap-leaf species.

The other terete vanda, *V. hookeriana*, has been involved in about 25 different crosses to date, fewer than for *V. teres*.

Among strap-leaf vandas, *V. coerulea* has been most popular as a parent. The blue color is usually transmitted to its offspring. More than 70 crosses involving *V. coerulea* have been registered. Probably the outstanding hybrids of this species have been *V.* Rothschildiana (*V. coerulea* X *V. sanderiana*) and *V.* Hilo Blue (*V. coerulea* X *V.* Bill Sutton). The recent increased interest in *V. coerulea* in Thailand has led to the selection of excellent forms and their use in hybridization; this should dramatically improve both species and hybrids.

V. denisoniana is now being used more frequently in crosses. Up to 1960, only five hybrids of *V. denisoniana* were registered. Since that time, 13 hybrids have appeared, including the intergeneric hybrids, *Aeridovanda*, *Ascocenda*, *Renantanda* and *Rhynchovanda*. Of particular significance is the occurrence of both diploid (2 N) and tetraploid (4 N) forms in nature. Rapee Sagarik crossed a tetraploid plant of the red *Rhy. gigantea* with both diploid and tetraploid forms of *V. denisoniana*. The 4N X 2N cross flowered first, with attractive dark-wine colored 3N offspring, and was registered as *Rhynchovanda* Sagarik Wine. The 4N X 4N flowered later, but with purplish-brown flowers. The 3N offspring contained two genomes of *Rhy. gigantea* and one genome of *V. denisoniana*, while the 4N offspring contained two genomes each of the two parental species. The dominant influence of *Rhy. gigantea* in the 3N offpsring is readily apparent. The 4N offspring has proved to be fertile, unlike the 3N offspring, and may be valuable for further breeding because of the balanced tetraploid or amphidiploid nature.

Other *Vanda* species of Thailand have been used sparingly to date, probably because they have not become generally known to the orchid world.

VANDOPSIS

Vandopsis is well known to orchidists specializing in vandaceous orchids, because one of its species, *Vandopsis lissochiloides*, although not a very attractive orchid in itself, has given rise to the outstanding intergeneric hybrid, *Renanopsis* Lena Rowold. The genus is closely allied to *Renanthera* and *Arachnis* and is made up of about 10 species that inhabit Southeast Asia. Thailand is represented by three species, *Vdps. lissochiloides*, *Vdps. gigantea* and *Vdps. parishii.*

Vandopsis lissochiloides (Gaud.) Pfitz.

This best known member of the genus, like many other orchids, has gone through several name changes. It was commonly called *Vanda batemanii* and was also designated at times as *Fieldia lissochiloides*, *Vanda lissochiloides* or *Stauropsis lissochiloides*. This is a robust orchid with a stem about 1 inch thick, which attains a height of several feet. The thick, leathery leaves measure about 16 by 2 inches and are unequally lobed. The rigidly erect and extremely long inflorescence, often 5 feet in length, produces 25 or more flowers during the blooming period, with 3 or 4 flowers open at a time. The delicately fragrant flowers are about 2 inches across. The thick petals and sepals are greenish yellow, spotted with reddish brown. The midlobe is fleshy and laterally flattened.

This orchid usually inhabits open grasslands in northeastern Thailand. It is also native to the Moluccas and the Philippines. It is relatively easy to cultivate and flowers well. It can be treated in the same manner as vandas but, because of the robust growth, its container should be large and sturdy, and the plants firmly staked.

Vandopsis gigantea (Ldl.) Pfitz.

The stem of this orchid is thick and relatively short, seldom exceeding 1 foot in height. The heavy, leathery leaves are about 14 by $2\frac{1}{2}$ inches. The inflorescence is short, arching or drooping, and usually carries from 7 to 15 flowers from April to June. The flowers are slightly fragrant, long-lasting, and about $2\frac{1}{2}$ inches across. Sepals and petals are broad and fleshy, with bold reddish brown blotches on a yellow background. The outer surfaces of the sepals are suffused with purple. The labellum is white with purplish markings.

This species comes from northern, southwestern and peninsular Thailand. Its natural distribution is from the Tenasserim Range in Burma and Thailand through peninsular Thailand to northern Malaysia. In the peninsular region, plants usually grow on rocks in the hills close to the sea. They can be handled as the vandas and grown in full sunlight.

Vandopsis parishii (Veitch & Rchb. f.) Schltr.

This orchid, commonly referred to as *Vanda parishii*, is by far the most attractive member of the genus. The short stems and broad, fleshy leaves, about 8 by 2½ inches, give the general appearance of a phalaenopsis. From March to May, the sub-erect inflorescence, up to 12 inches long, carries 6 to 12 flowers arranged in two rows. The round, full flowers measure 2 inches across. The thick, broad, overlapping sepals and petals are brownish purple, light lavender toward the base and white at the base. The labellum varies from orchid-purple to greenish purple. This is the variety, *marriottiana*, which prevails in Thailand. It usually flowers from March to May, with individual flowers lasting about 2 weeks. Infrequently, flowers with greenish yellow sepals and petals spotted with dark purple are found.

Vdps. parishii is an epiphyte, inhabiting deciduous forest at fairly high elevations. In Thailand it is found in eastern, northeastern, northern and western regions. It is also distributed in neighboring Indochina and Burma. Brought down to low elevations in the tropics, it is very difficult to cultivate and rarely flowers. It requires an environment somewhat similar to that of *Vanda coerulea*.

Vandopsis hybrids

Vandopsis species have been hybridized only within the last three decades. The rate of hybridizing *Vdps. lissochiloides* with various vandas to produce the intergeneric opsisandas has, however, been intense. *Opsisanda* Colombo (*Vanda dearei* X *Vdps. lissochiloides*), the first hybrid registered in 1947, was followed by *Opsisanda* Singapore (*V. insignis* X *Vdps. lissochiloides*) in 1949. In the fifties, 19 opsisandas involving *Vdps. lissochiloides* as a parent appeared in rapid succession, and 5 others were registered in the sixties. *Vdps. gigantea* has produced six *Opsisanda* hybrids. It may be of interest to note that the third *Vandopsis* species of Thailand, *Vdps. parishii*, has not produced a single hybrid with *Vanda*, although for some time it went under the name of *Vanda parishii*.

Among other intergeneric hybrids involving *Vandopsis*, probably *Renanopsis* Lena Rowald (*Vdps. lissochiloides* X *Renanthera storiei*) has been the most popular, with its long, branching, horizontal sprays of striking red blossoms. Several plants of this cross have received the Award of Merit from various orchid societies. *Vdps. gigantea* and *Vdps. parishii* have also produced some *Renanopsis* hybrids. *Renanopsis* Pele is the first successful hybrid of *Vdps. parishii*.

A few *Vandachnis* hybrids (*Vandopsis* X *Arachnis*) have appeared. In addition, *Phalandopsis* (*Phalaenopsis* X *Vandopsis*), *Opsistylis* (*Vandopsis* X *Rhynchostylis*), *Trichopsis* (*Trichoglottis* X *Vandopsis*) and the trigeneric *Laycockara* (*Arachnis* X *Phalaenopsis* X *Vandopsis*) have been produced.

77

ORCHID COLLECTING TRIP–KHAOKHIEO AND KHAOYAI, 1962

On a Friday afternoon in October, we left Bangkok for a weekend orchid collecting expedition, led by Tem Smitinand, Keeper of the Forest Herbarium.

The weather was ominous with dark, threatening clouds, for this was about the end of the monsoon season when the rains are usually heaviest. We soon ran into a downpour, and the canvas side covers of our Jeep were not adequate to keep out the rain.

At that time, the road was full of holes, but at Saraburi we got on the Friendship Highway, a beautiful road completed only a few years earlier.

We spent the night at the Forestry Department resthouse in Pakchong, and the next morning we switched to a Land Rover and headed for Khaoyai (*khao* is mountain, and *yai* is big). This government forestry conservation area had recently been developed into a national park.

An hour's drive brought us to the Forestry Station, and by 10 a.m. we were ready to begin our climb up Khaokhieo (green mountain), about 2700 feet above sea level. The government was cutting a road to the top of Khaokhieo, and we were able to drive some distance up the mountain. When we reached the point no longer passable for the Land Rover, we continued on foot. The recently cleared road offered an excellent opportunity to collect orchids, for they were attached to large trunks of felled trees and would have been inaccessible to us in their natural state.

A short walk brought us to a large felled tree covered with numerous types of orchids – *Eria*, *Podochilus*, *Bulbophyllum*, *Oberonia*, *Dendrobium* and *Sarcanthus*. We collected most of the orchid plants on this, because they would have been destroyed by the time the road was completed. This area is a tropical rain forest with very lush growth and trees towering 60 to 80 feet. Looking up into the trees, we saw large clumps of *Dendrobium revolutum*, *Coelogyne* sp. and others, but we had no intention of climbing those tall trees.

As we went along, we saw species of *Liparis*, *Thrixspermum*, *Porpax*, dendrobiums belonging to *Nigrohirsutae*, *Eugenanthe*, *Aporum* and other sections, *Cymbidium*, *Appendicula*, *Oberonia*, etc. Various ferns, members of Zingiberaceae, *Hoya*, *Esculentis*, *Somerilla* and other plants also attracted our attention.

At noon, we came to a clear stream where we rested and ate the lunch brought by Mr. Boomruang, the forestry officer at Khaoyai. On a large, low rock beside the stream were several clumps of *Habenaria rhodocheila*, a species with attractive scarlet flowers.

78

While we were eating, Tem Smitinand was pushing up the hill, collecting various plant species. We learned that he usually went without lunch on these collecting trips in order to gather plants, and we realized how physically active a taxonomist must be to perform his work.

From this point on, we had to climb without benefit of a path cleared by a bulldozer. As we approached the summit, the grade became steeper, sometimes sloping 45 to 60 degrees, a bit taxing on sedentary bodies unaccustomed to such rigorous activity. We reached the top at 2 p.m., and perched ourselves on large boulders to rest and enjoy the gorgeous mountain scenery. The cool invigorating mountain air permitted a rapid recuperation, and we were able to collect several sarcanthine orchids in this summit area.

Going down was much faster and easier than climbing up, but fatigue was beginning to set in when we reached our Land Rover. By 4 p.m. we were at the Forestry Resthouse, where we washed with cold rain water. Mr. Smitinand was busy preparing herbarium specimens of the collected material while Mr. Boomruang prepared a sumptuous Thai dinner.

The following morning we went on a 2-hour hike along a river in the Khaoyai area. On this trail we found orchids similar to those types in Khaokhieo.

Most of the orchids observed and collected at Khaoyai and Khaokhieo might be considered of botanical and taxonomic interest but of little horticultural value, due to their relatively small, inconspicuous flowers. However, these species were of special interest to us because of our investigations on the cytology of orchid species.

Interestingly, certain sarcanthine orchids, such as *Thrixspermum* and *Sarcanthus*, grew in dense, shaded areas ; others, such as *Dendrobium revolutum*, *Eria* and *Coelogyne*, were found on tall exposed trees. Trees along streams seemed relatively rich with orchids. Also, certain types of trees appeared more suited for orchid growth than others. This suitability is probably related to the texture of the bark and the amount of sunlight filtering through the foliage and branches. Some trees were laden with numerous types of orchids, while neighboring trees had none. A relatively small tree was covered with many *Coelogyne* plants, amidst trees with no orchid plants.

An important dividend of this trip was the acquisition of several orchid species to be used in orchid cytology research to expand the knowledge of species relationships of sarcanthine and dendrobium orchids.

ORCHIDS NEAR CHANDHABURI EXPERIMENT STATION, 1963

Chandhaburi, a province in southeastern Thailand, is separated from Cambodia by relatively wet, densely forested mountain ranges. The rich alluvial valleys of this region are well adapted for the culture of such delectable tropical fruits as rambutan, durian and mangosteen. The Department of Agriculture has established an experiment station, principally for fruit research, in this important fruit-growing area. Chandhaburi is also well known for its black sapphire deposits and reed handicrafts.

Although the major purpose of our trip to Chandhaburi was to observe the facilities and researches of the Priew Agricultural Experiment Station as well as the general horticultural activities of the region, we were able to observe and collect orchid species in readily accessible area.

We left Bangkok around 6 : 30 a.m. on February 18, 1963. We took a station wagon, for there is a good highway to Chandhaburi. About 75 miles from Bangkok, just past the seaside resort of Bangsaen, we stopped to see the Siracha Student Training Farm of Kasetsart University, then drove on to Suttaheep. There, Mr. Kumhang, a former farm leader who went to the United States on an observation-study grant, was successfully growing a relatively new crop of Thailand -- grapes. He had several acres under cultivation and was most enthusiastic over the prospects, for the fruit was commanding a premium price due to its novelty and scarcity.

After lunch, we drove on through the Rayong region, where cassava is cultivated extensively, and arrived in Chandhaburi at 3 p.m. After a brief tour of the town, we arrived at the Priew Station where we were to spend two nights at the Station guesthouse.

Having an hour or so of daylight remaining, we decided to look for some native orchid species in the immediate vicinity. The Station is located at the foot of a hill leading into the mountain range that forms a beautiful backdrop. A short walk into woods brought us to an old, abandoned rubber planting. There, attached to the trunks of rubber and other volunteer trees in a densely shaded area, were several attractive flowering specimens of *Dendrobium farmeri*, a member of the *Callista* section in the genus *Dendrobium*. Also, growing high atop the branches of durian trees, perhaps 60 feet high, were large clumps of *Den. friedericksianum* with a profusion of blooms. Both types, yellow with and without the purple blotches on the lip, were growing side by side, indicating that this genetic variation should not be a basis for botanical variety distinction. This species, belonging to the nobile group of dendrobiums, is endemic to this region. At low elevations it should be much easier to cultivate and flower than others of the nobile group and, therefore, might play a valuable role in producing

80

nobile-type hybrids for the lowlands.

Within a period of 45 minutes we collected two horticulturally desirable *Dendrobium* species. Some botanicals, such as *Coelogyne trinervis, Den. leonis,* and *Bulbophyllum* sp., were also observed.

In the afternoon of the following day, the Chief of the Station drove us to a nearby waterfall, where he had observed plants of *Renanthera coccinea* growing in the trees above the waterfall. We were most eager to observe this species in its natural state, but we searched in vain. This waterfall had become a tourist attraction, and had been completely stripped of this species. However, we were able to find a few plants that were identified later when they flowered as *Phalaenopsis (Kingiella) decumbens,* one of the two *Phalaenopsis* species known to exist in Thailand.

It is fortunate that such an experiment station in Chandhaburi exists, where a few minutes walk beyond its boundary leads to forests in which beautiful native orchids can be viewed in their natural splendor.

COLLECTING ORCHIDS IN KHANBURI FORESTS*, 1963

In March 1963, we had a most exciting and profitable experience of observing and collecting orchid species in the forests of Khanburi which lie west of Bangkok and near the Burmese border. During the 6-day expedition, we traveled by Land Rovers, Jeeps, boats and railway scooter with trailer, and were lodged in forestry resthouses, a logging camp, a mining camp and a small village.

Included in the expedition were Dean Thiem Komkris, J. D. Sinclair, Sanga Sabhasri, Vallobh Norabhallop and Prabhand Koysomboon, of the Faculty of Forestry, and H. Kamemoto, Rapee Sagarik and Sangtham Komkris of the Horticulture Department, Kasetsart University. The forestry staff members were primarily interested in observing watersheds and other forest problems of the region, while the horticulturists were mainly concerned with observing and collecting orchids and other plants of horticultural value.

We left Bangkok around 8 a.m. in two Land Rovers and stopped at Ban Pong Forestry Station to meet Mr. Prasert, Division Forest Officer, who had made all arrangements for the trip and was to accompany us. We drove to the city of Khanburi, 68 miles from Bangkok. A weapons carrier truck, which was to have transported our food and other necessities for the trip, developed brake trouble, and a Jeep had to be substituted.

When we departed at 2 p.m., our expedition had added two Jeeps and, besides Mr. Prasert, a few helpers, including a cook and an experienced tree climber.

Our first overnight stop was Erawan National Park, which was still entirely undeveloped. The road was rugged and, in many spots, impassable to ordinary passenger vehicles. The parched forests of this area were predominantly bamboo, with a few scattered trees. Relatively few orchids were seen enroute to the park — *Aerides mitrata* with nearly terete, pendulous leaves, *Rhynchostylis coelestis* with closely spaced conduplicate leaves, and the ubiquitous *Cymbidium finlaysonianum*.

We reached our destination around 6 p.m. and immediately prepared ourselves for the night by bathing, making our beds and putting up mosquito nets, for we were now in the forests far from the comforts of the city. But for our dinner, as well as for all meals during the trip, Mr. Prasert had brought an assortment of food and the necessary equipment to prepare sumptuous meals. The large block of ice, brought from Khanburi,

---

*Revision of the article which appeared in the American Orchid Society Bulletin 33 : 132—138. 1964.

lasted 4 days and was much appreciated, particularly during the day, when the dry air parched our throats.

Early the next morning we took a short walk to the waterfalls while breakfast was being prepared. This spot boasts 51 successive waterfalls of various sizes and forms, which makes it an ideal area for development into a recreational park. We had time to see only the three waterfalls nearest camp. The only orchid we saw was a large clump of a sarcanthine orchid, which probably had escaped collection by previous visitors because of its small, inconspicuous flowers.

We left the Erawan Forestry Station at 9 a.m. and headed deeper into the forest toward the Forest Industry Logging Camp at Phu Klang Dong, situated approximately 2000 feet above sea level. A few miles from Erawan National Park and still in a forest of bamboo, we saw a large, old, fallen tree supporting many plants of *Vanda lilacina* and *Rhynchostylis coelestis*, which we added to our growing collection. About 28 miles from Erawan, we spotted a large clump of *Staurochilus* (*Trichoglottis*) *fasciatus* growing on a tree trunk only 10 feet from the ground. After gathering the plants, we noticed numerous *Pomatocalpa spicata* growing on a smaller tree which provided heavier shade to the orchids. On a neighboring tree, we found several leafless sarcanthine orchid plants which were later identified as *Chilochista usnoides*.

We continued on to the Kwei Yai River, where the cars had to be transported across on a bamboo raft towed by a motor boat. Across the river was Sri Sawasdi, a village with a population of about 400. The kitchen brigade immediately started our lunch. The skies darkened rapidly, and a few raindrops were followed by a downpour accompanied by thunder and lightning. This first rain of the year ruined our original plan to reach the logging camp, another 10 miles away, for the roads were now impassable. There was also the possibility of our being stranded in this village for a day or two, depending on the severity of the downpour. Fortunately, the rain stopped around 5 : 30 p.m. Some of us bathed and swam in the river. A house owned by a mining company was our abode for the night.

The road was still muddy and unserviceable in the morning, so we had time for a stroll through the village to see some orchids the villagers were growing. The cultivation of *Vanda coerulea*, *V. teres*, *Vandopsis parishii*, *Rhynchostylis retusa*, *Aerides mitrata*, *Aer. crassifolia* and *Dendrobium pulchellum* gave an excellent indication of the species of horticultural value available in this region.

By 10 a.m. the clouds had broken and the sun shone through, so we resumed our trip. The forest now, instead of bamboo, was mainly made up of dipterocarps and other deciduous trees. After an hour's drive we began to see more orchids, many of which were of horticultural interest. We stopped by a tree covered with many plants of *Den. dixanthum*, with flowers somewhat similar to those of *Den. aggregatum*. *Den. moschatum*, *Phalaenopsis cornu-cervi* and *Coelogyne* sp. were also collected. High up on another tree, beyond the reach of our climber, was a beautiful flowering specimen of *Vdps. parishii*.

A little farther along the road we saw a large clump of *Den. chrysotoxum*, one of the attractive members of the *Callista* section of *Dendrobium*, which had pseudobulbs about 2 inches in diameter, bearing several spikes with buds. This was growing only 15 feet from the ground. A few plants of *Den. thyrsiflorum* were also observed. In a few minutes we were able to add to our collection specimens of *Den. aggregatum*, *Den. moschatum*, *Den. nobile*, *Vdps. parishii*, and several unidentified species of *Coelogyne*, *Bulbophyllum*, *Pholidota*, etc.

We reached the logging camp of the Forestry Industry Organization in time for a brief rest and lunch. Then a short drive brought us to a spot rich with orchids. The prize find was the epiphytic *Paphiopedilum parishii*. We gathered numerous large clumps growing in the crotches of branches or on the upper surfaces of trunks of inclined trees. A few plants of *V. coerulea*, growing high up on trees, also were collected, thanks to the agile and daring climber of the Forestry Department. We also found *Den. parishii*, the diminutive *Den. crepidatum*, and specimens of other species collected earlier. Soon we had several baskets of orchids. The abundance of orchids in this area was undoubtedly due to the inaccessibility of the region. Even during the dry months, road conditions did not permit easy access, and when the rains came, the entire area was completely cut off to road traffic.

After dinner and a hurried bath in cold stream water, we were ready to retire for the night. The resthouse had a low, galvanized sheet-iron roof, a sloping floor made of flattened bamboo poles, and a completely open front. A thin reed mat was the only bedding. The night was extremely chilly, and a single blanket was not adequate to keep out the cold. We slept in our clothes and jackets, but even these were insufficient. The cold weather clearly indicated the prevailing environmental conditions in which orchids thrive. During these dry months, the trees lose their leaves, exposing the orchids to the heat, light and drought, but the night temperatures drop to the fifties, and probably much lower during January and February -- factors which favor their flowering.

The following morning we were scheduled to leave for Thong Pha Phum immediately after breakfast, but since orchids were plentiful in the forestry camp area, we allowed another 2 hours for collecting. We went in a different direction from the previous day. A watershed area — a dense evergreen forest — harbored a few sarcanthine orchids, mostly of botanical interest. Once out of this dense forest, we found *Den. pulchellum* in full bloom, as well as *Rhy. retusa* and *Aer. crassifolia*.

By this time we had about half a dozen baskets full of orchids. We loaded the orchids into the two vehicles that came with us from Bangkok, and sent them back to Khanburi to await our return. A truck was hired to carry our supplies.

Between Nern Sawan and Thong Pha Phum, on trees providing considerable shade along a river, we collected *Robiquetia spathulata*, *Sarcanthus appendiculatus*, another *Sarcanthus* sp. and a *Dendrobium* sp. belonging to the *Aporum* section. Again, our previous observations were confirmed, that in dense shade, particularlarly along streams, most of the orchid species are of botanical rather than of horticultural interest.

We came to another open bamboo forest that was interspersed with a few tall trees. The large, lavender flowers of *V. teres*, growing on a large, fallen tree, attracted our attention. A brief stop rewarded us with several plants of *Den. pierardii*, *Rhy. retusa* and *Cym. finlaysonianum*, besides the *V. teres*. Along the road and high up on trees, we saw many more *V. teres* in full bloom.

Late in the afternoon, we came to the bank of the River Kwei Noi. There was a large self-service raft to accommodate the cars, but none of us had any experience in handling a raft with bamboo poles against the current. Fortunately, the drivers and other help were able to get all three vehicles across. From there to Thong Pha Phum, we had to make several detours, ploughing through mud and water from recent rains. Our destination was a thriving village on the bank of the river.

Here, some of us visited a private collection of an assortment of species of the area, including *Den. infundibulum* collected from the deep jungle valley, *Den. densiflorum* and *Ascocentrum ampullaceum*.

The following morning we packed our supplies and orchids and ourselves into four hired motor boats and began our voyage down the River Kwei Noi. This was by far the most pleasant and picturesque portion of our journey. In about 3 hours, we arrived at the resthouse of the Royal Forestry Department at Sai Yoke, famed for the waterfall that attracts countless vacationers each year. We were greeted by Mr. Prasert's wife, who had come up the river with fresh food supplies.

After lunch we had a short siesta, for it was very hot. At 3 p.m. we went down the river on our final orchid safari of this trip. High above, on the sides of a cliff, we spotted many plants of *Den. moschatum*, with the reddish leaves characteristic of plants exposed to drought and sunlight. We climbed the hill in the sweltering heat and collected a few clumps clinging to a large boulder. On a grooved portion of a large boulder which had gathered some humus and leaf mold, we saw two deciduous *Calanthe* species, one of which was identified as *Cal. rubens*. Also in the vicinity, we collected *Pomatocalpa spicata*, *Luisia* sp., *Phalaenopsis decumbens*, *Oberonis* sp. and *Vanilla* sp.

We left Sai Yoke the following morning and 2 hours later arrived at Kaeng La Wah, which boasts of a large cave with stalactites. The hot weather was not conducive to climbing the hill to reach the cave, but realizing that we might not get here again, we took advantage of the opportunity.

After lunch on the floating restaurant (house built on bamboo rafts), we boarded our boats again and moved down river for another 2 hours.

From Wang Pho to Khanburi, another 34 miles, we went by rail, but not by a conventional train. Mr. Prasert had arranged for a motor-driven railway scooter with a trailer attached, just large enough to accommodate the entire party and belongings, including the valuable orchid collection. The scooter made good time, although at every joint in the rail, the trailer would bounce up and down. On this leg of our trip we passed under the bridge on the River Kwai.

85

At the railway station at Khanburi, the two vehicles that we had sent back from Phu Klang Dong and a station wagon from Bangkok were awaiting our arrival. It was 6 : 30 p.m., so we had our dinner in Khanburi ; 2 hour's drive brought us back to Bangkok, culminating a wonderful orchid collecting expedition.

It was a most exciting and highly educational experience to observe the numerous horticulturally desirable species of orchids growing in their natural habitats, to study their ecology and growth characteristics, and to assemble these species at Kasetsart University for scientific purposes. Considering that orchids had been collected continuously for the past several decades in Thailand, we were pleasantly surprised to find so many still available in abundance in the wilds. Of course, this trip was particularly fruitful because we were in areas not readily accsssible to orchid collectors and, therefore, not yet fully exploited.

CHIENGMAI ORCHIDS AND THE SONGKRAN FESTIVAL, 1963

Chiengmai, a thriving city in northern Thailand, lies in a large valley surrounded by mountains, at a latitude of 19° N and an elevation of 1023 feet. The climate, much cooler than that of Bangkok, is suitable for the culture of the many native orchid species of the region. Here, *Vanda coerulea* is widely cultivated, and each year during its flowering season in August, a spectacular orchid show is staged for the public. In April, usually coinciding with Songkran, the local New Year Festival which attracts throngs of visitors from Bangkok and other parts of the country, a display features such beautiful orchids as *V. denisoniana, Dendrobium chrysotoxum, Den. thyrsiflorum, Den. aggregatum, Den. pierardii, Den. nobile, Ascocentrum curvifolium*, and *Vandopsis parishii*. At the orchid show held in Chiengmai in April 1963, a magnificent specimen plant of *Den. chrysotoxum* measured 3 feet wide, with about 75 sprays each carrying from 15 to 20 flowers. Also a large specimen of *Den. pierardii* had numerous pendulant pseudobulbs covered by a mass of delicate, lilac-colored blossoms.

Numerous plants of *Rhynchostylis coelestis* grow on teak trees lining some streets within the city. From Chiengmai, you can travel in almost any direction into the hills or mountains and see a number of orchid species growing in their natural habitats.

Hod to Mesarieng

The Dean of the Forestry Faculty of Kasetsart University arranged for us to accompany the forestry group on an overnight trip to Mesarieng, which lies about 140 miles southwest of Chiengmai. The new highway from Hod to Ban Kong Loey, which was opened a year earlier, cut through virgin forests and afforded an excellent opportunity for observing and collecting orchid species.

Enroute to Hod, about 55 miles from Chiengmai, we traveled through fields of soybeans, peanuts and tobacco — the second crop of the region following the rice crop — and came to the Chom Thong Temple, noted for its Buddha's Relic. From Hod the road gradually climbed and soon we came to another tourist attraction, Orb Luang (large gorge). As we drove along we saw some flowering orchids perched high on trees. Upon close examination, they were identified as *Den. draconis* and *Den. cariniferum* of the *Nigrohirsutae* section. After a short walk into the forest, we came across *Den. secundum, Sarcanthus kunstleri, Phalaenopsis cornu-cervi, Vdps. parishii, Aer. crassifolia, Rhy. gigantea* var. *illustre*, and *Luisia* sp. besides the two *Dendrobium* species observed earlier.

The highway was completed as far as Ban Kong Loey, but from there to Mesarieng, the 34-mile road cut through the mountainside was narrow, dusty, winding and treacherous, allowing only one-way traffic throughout most of the way. It took 3 hours of rough and uncomfortable driving to reach the forestry resthouse in this remote town.

Mesarieng has a population of about 30,000, many of whom belong to the Yang hill tribe. In wet weather this town was completely inaccessible by road. An airport is in operation, but during the rainy season the rain and fog often prevent planes from landing or departing, so the town may be completely isolated for a month or more.

The best way to see the produce of an area is to visit the morning market. We arrived at the marketplace at 6 a.m., primarily to see the orchids. Flowering plants, many with a single pseudobulb, obviously for use as cut-flower decoration, were on sale. *Den. draconis* and *Den. tortile* were available. Surprisingly, there was a brisk trade in orchids by the local population, and within a half hour the entire lot was sold. We learned that the per capita consumption of flowers in Mesarieng far exceeded that of Bangkok.

We left Mesarieng around 9 a.m. and stopped in an open, deciduous forest area, where we were able to collect specimens of *Den. cariniferum, Den. chrysotoxum* and a flowering plant of *Pleione (Coelogyne) schilleriana.*

After lunch at Ban Kong Loey, we headed back to Chiengmai. On the main highway we stopped our car near the 40-kilometer post, at an elevation of approximately 3600 feet, for the final collection of this trip. A short trek into the sparsely populated, deciduous forest revealed an abundance of *Den. draconis, Den. cariniferum* and *Den. pulchellum.* A terrestrial *Cymbidium* and several botanicals, such as *Bulbophyllum, Eulophia, Luisia* and *Eria,* were also found.

About a year later, in March 1964, we made a 1-day trip from Chiengmai to Ban Kong Loey and stopped at the 37-, 49- and 52-kilometer posts from Hod to observe and collect orchids. *Den. cariniferum* and *Den. draconis* were still plentiful and in peak bloom. A few flowering plants of *Den. bellatulum,* belonging to the *Nigrohirsutae* section, were encountered. *Den. pulchellum* was also in season. Other orchids seen were *Den. secundum, Bulbophyllum, Eria* and *Pholidota.*

Den. draconis, Den. cariniferum and *Den. pulchellum* were widely distributed but were not in great demand by the local orchidists. This probably accounts for the abundance of plants in such readily accessible areas. However, as more people become interested in orchid growing, indiscriminate collecting will eventually lead to scarcity and perhaps complete depletion of orchids in these heavily populated areas.

Farng

In Farng, about 90 miles north of Chiengmai and at an elevation of 2700 feet, the Department of Agriculture has developed an experiment station that seems eminently suited to the culture of subtropical horticultural crops.

On April 8, 1963, we left Chiengmai at 8 a.m. The first 31 miles were paved but the balance was rough and dusty. Many orchids could be seen attached to the trunks and branches of trees along the highway. We reached the station in Farng at noon and ate our lunch beside a stream of cool, clear water.

Adjoining the station is a forest reservation area which has several hot springs. In this sparsely vegetated area we observed the leafless sarcanthine orchid, *Chilochista lunifera*. It was even found growing on wooden fence posts. *Den. pierardii* was in full splendor. *V. teres* was in bloom high atop the trees. We also found *Den. aggregatum*, *Rhy. retusa* and *Luisia* sp. We returned to Chiengmai that evening.

Doi Saked

The next morning we were scheduled to leave early with our forestry friends for Doi Saked, about 9 miles east of Chiengmai, but a thunderstorm delayed our departure until 10 a.m. We packed our gear in a Jeep and a Land Rover and started on our journey. We stopped briefly at Maejo Vocational School, Maejo Tobacco Experiment Station, with its impressive laboratories and greenhouses, and Maejo Agricultural Experiment Station where we had lunch.

When we got off the asphalt feeder road into the forests, traveling became rough, the road puddled with water from earlier rains. The vehicles had to plough through mud and cross streams about 1 foot deep to reach our destination.

The first orchids we saw were *Rhy. coelestis* and *V. lilacina*, growing on bare, dead branches, fully exposed to the sun. As we climbed we began to see *Aer. crassifolia* growing on deciduous dipterocarps. Because of the drought and the exposure to the sun, the leaves of this orchid were wrinkled and reddish purple. Passing through a slightly denser growth of trees, we observed *Robiquetia spathulata* and small plants of *Den. aggregatum* and *Sarcanthus* sp.

We stopped our car on a knoll in a relatively open, dry, infertile area with dwarfed gnarled growths of dipterocarps and bare, eroded soil. Orchids were in abundance, but they were also yellow and stunted. On old, stunted trees, easily reached from the ground, were many small flowering plants of *Aer. crassifolia*, *Aer. multiflora*, *Den. draconis* and *V. brunnea*, besides a terete-leaved *Sarcanthus* and other botanicals. Since night was approaching, we had to continue our trip, but hoped to stop in this area on our way back.

We reached our destination in Huay Mae Warn around 6 : 30 p.m. -- a schoolhouse left vacant for the summer. A tent was pitched to serve as kitchen.

The following morning after breakfast, while our sack lunches were being prepared, we went for a short stroll. On a large tree trunk was a beautiful spray of small, clear chartreuse flowers of the leafless *Chilochista lunifera*, and also plants of *Luisia* and *Coelogyne*.

About 3 hours of driving over hills and valleys brought us to Doi Nang Keo, at 4000 feet elevation and bordering Chiengrai Province. We began to climb the mountain ridge on foot. After a few minutes of walking in relatively dense shade, we observed several clumps of flowering *Den. thyrsiflorum* on the trunks of very tall trees. The attractive flowers of this species have pure white sepals and petals and a contrasting bright-yellow labellum, and are densely arranged in a pendulous inflorescence. As we hiked farther, we came across *Cymbidium* sp., *Den. parishii*, *Vanda* sp., *Luisia* sp. and *Sarcanthus* sp. A large clump of

89

Coelogyne trinervis completely covered a large boulder.   *Den. aggregatum* was observed in a relatively dense forest growth.

At Doi Pa Tung, in an open deciduous forest interspersed with some bamboo clumps, we observed *Asctm. miniatum*, with its small but brilliant orange-yellow flowers. Nearby on a tall tree, was a large clump of *Aer. falcata*. On our way back along a slightly different route, we came across several plants of *Rhy. retusa* growing on tall trees.   These plants are larger and have broader leaves than those from other regions of Thailand.

We returned to the schoolhouse at Huay Mae Warn at dusk to spend another night in the mountains.

On our way back to Chiengmai the following morning, we stopped once again in the vicinity where we had collected the first day. In only 2 days, the forest had been transformed, for now the dipterocarps had sent out their new foliage, providing considerable shade to the orchids. We encountered more plants of *Aer. multiflora* and *Aer. odorata*. Additional plants of *Den. secundum, Den. draconis, Aer. flabellata, V. brunnea* and *Sarcanthus* sp. were added to our collection before we left the forests of Chiengmai.

THE DISAPPEARING ORCHIDS OF PRACHUAB, 1963, 1964 and 1973

A tip from Dr. Thavorn Vajrabhaya, cytogeneticist and orchidologist at Chulalongkorn University, that *Doritis pulcherrima* could be found off the highway in Prachuab, led to an overnight trip in quest of this species in August 1963.

We left Bangkok early one morning, crossed the bridge over the Chao Phya River to Dhonburi, then headed west on Highway 4 to Nakorn Pathom, famous for the largest chedi in Thailand. We veered south, passed through Rajburi, and stopped for lunch in Petchburi, 100 miles from Bangkok. This region supported many palmyra palm groves, presumably of native origin. In these groves, numerous clumps of *Cymbidium finlaysonianum* were clinging tenaciously to bare tree trunks. A machete was needed to bring down a few plants. This species produces long, pendulant inflorescences, with greenish brown flowers measuring about 1 ½ inches across, usually from May to August.

Another 30 miles south brought us to Huahin, a popular seaside resort with one of the finest beaches in Thailand. We proceeded to the 302-kilometer marker in Prachuab, where the species in quest was supposedly located. We parked our station wagon and entered the scrubby forest with patches of thickets interspersed among clear spots that may have been old rice paddies. The shrubs or stunted trees were 10 to 12 feet high, many with vicious thorns that made the thickets almost impenetrable.

Under a group of shrubs in a well-shaded area, about 30 yards in from the highway, we found a few clumps of flowering *Dor. pulcherrima* growing in sandy soil mixed with partially decayed leaves. Farther on, plants were small and unthrifty due to the dry conditions, but most of them had initiated flower spikes and several were in flower. The color of the flowers was highly variable, ranging from near white to dark purple. Unlike those from Prachinburi in eastern Thailand, the petals and sepals were excessively reflexed. In the same area, *Vanda teres* was growing in abundance.

Since it was getting late, we checked into our lodging at Prachuab beach, where the Thai Government had several reasonably priced rental bungalows. With the mountains and islands forming a backdrop for the expansive, gently curving beach, the beauty of the scenery was beyond description.

Early next morning we started our return trip. We stopped to explore in the vicinity of the 318-kilometer post. A short distance from the highway, we located several plants of *Rhynchostylis coelestis* growing on exposed branches of stunted trees. Clambering on some bushes were many plants of *Staurochilus* (*Trichoglottis*) *fasciatus*, some of which we added to our collection. *Dendrobium delacourii* and *Eulophia keithii* were also plentiful.

We stopped once again at the 302-kilometer post and were surprised to see

91

plants of *Dor. pulcherrima* in the bushes just off the highway. About 10 yards from the highway, many healthy plants of *Staur. fasciatus* were growing out of the thickets. We collected a few more specimens and returned to Bangkok.

A year later, in August 1964, we revisited the Prachuab area on our return from Ranong and Chumporn. Again we stopped at the 302-kilometer post and found plants of *Dor. pulcherrima* growing on the ground in the same spot. The plants were much healthier than the previous year probably due to more rains; the shrubs and other vegetation also were greener and thriftier. *V. teres* had multiplied greatly during the year.

Robust plants of *Staur. fasciatus* were seen growing out of the thickets. We were surprised to see so many plants still available just off the highway. Perhaps orchid collectors had not become aware of the existence of these orchids. We noticed also that, despite the relatively unfavorable soil and weather conditions for farming, the area was slowly being developed and cultivated, which meant that in a few years the whole region would be denuded of wild orchid species.

About 100 yards from the highway, we saw a branched spray of dark-red flowers arising from a sarcanthine orchid growing in a thicket. From a distance, it resembled *Renanthera coccinea*, although the plant and flowers appeared a bit small for that species. We tried to get close enough to photograph and collect the plants, but the vicious thorns of the shrubs and the many militant red ants made it difficult. A close examination of this interesting specimen showed that it was neither *Ren. coccinea* nor *Ren. matutina*. The flowers were much smaller than those of *Ren. coccinea*, and the lateral sepals were narrow toward the base and abruptly broadened and curved outward from about midpoint of the sepals. Could it possibly be a hitherto unrecorded *Renanthera* species of Thailand ?

Later, we sent some fresh material of this orchid to Dr. Holttum, at Kew Gardens, for identification. He concluded that it differed from other described species of *Renanthera* and gave it a new name, *Renanthera isosepala*. Thus, only a few yards off the main highway, we collected an attractive new orchid species from Thailand.

Nine years later, in April 1973, we made a 1-day visit to Prachuab to determine the status of the native orchid species. The new Thonburi-Paktho highway, which had just opened, bypasses Nakorn Pathom and Rajburi and connects with Highway 4 near Petchburi, shortening the distance from Bangkok to Huahin by 32 kilometers.

We drove directly to the 302-kilometer post area which had harbored *Doritis pulcherrima*. The orchids that had been growing just off the highway had completely disappeared. This region had become an important pineapple production center, and much of the land had been cleared.

The 318-kilometer post area had not yet been developed. The stunted trees and shrubs still supported many *Rhynchostylis coelestis*, which were in bloom. We also saw thick stands of the terrestrial orchid, *Eulophia keithii*. However, *Trichoglottis fasciata* and *Renanthera isosepala*, which were once plentiful in this area, had been depleted by orchid collectors.

RANONG–THE HOME OF DENDROBIUM FORMOSUM, 1964

Ranong, in peninsular Thailand, is the native habitat of *Dendrobium formosum* var. *giganteum*, one of the finest members of the *Nigrohirsutae* section of *Dendrobium*.

The major objectives of our trip in August 1964 were to observe the ecology of this species and to investigate the horticultural crops of the region. We left Bangkok in a Jeep station wagon, headed for the peninsula. Just before entering Petchburi, we passed a familiar orchidaceous sight -- plants of *Cymbidium finlaysonianum* attached to trunks of palmyra palms. We drove on through Huahin to Prachuab, but deferred exploration of this area until our return trip. We visited the Klong Wan Fisheries Station of the Department of Fisheries, where Kasetsart University had constructed student quarters and a guest cottage and had begun developing ponds for brackish-water fish-culture experiments.

The next morning, as we neared Chumporn, we saw *Cym. finlaysonianum* on trunks of palmyra palms, even more numerous than at Petchburi. Two very large plants of *Grammatophyllum speciosum* were growing among the cymbidiums.

In the early afternoon, we met the Chief of the Ranong Rubber Experiment Station, a Kasetsart University graduate, who directed us to the Sawee Experiment Station, about 18 miles south of Chumporn. This relatively new experiment station of the Department of Agriculture was developed primarily for research on coconuts. Tangerines, durians, rambutans and other fruits also were being investigated.

We began our search for *Den. formosum* the next day. The road to Ranong was predominantly paved, but it wound up and down the mountainside to reach the western side of the peninsula. Along the way we spotted a few plants of *Spathoglottis spicata* in flowers — both dark and light purple forms. When we reached the Ranong Rubber Station, the Chief of the Station offered to guide us to the habitat of *Den. formosum*. Just before reaching Ranong, we visited an orchid grower who was cultivating orchid species of the region. He said that most of his orchids came from Burma, which is separated from Ranong by a river. He showed us some *Den. formosum*, *Den. farmeri*, *Den. densiflorum*, *Renanthera coccinea*, *Rhynchostylis retusa* and two species of *Calanthe*. The grower claimed that his *Rhy. retusa* plants were the white form, collected from deep forests in Burma.

Past Ranong, about 390 miles from Bangkok, we entered a side road recently cut open by the Highway Department. The lush, dense, tropical rain forests attested to the claim that Ranong is one of the wettest areas of Thailand. We stopped at the Highway Department camp to look for orchids. High up on tall evergreen trees, we spotted some plants of *Den. formosum*, but not having a professional climber, it was virtually impossible to gather the plants. Instead, we looked for plants on recently felled trees. Most of the

93

plants found were small. We also found a few plants each of *Rhy. retusa* and *Aerides odorata*.

Driving back toward the main highway, we saw a clump of a sarcanthine orchid on a short tree. On close examination, it was determined to be *Aer. odorata*. On a neighboring tree we saw several plants of *Den. formosum* and *Den. secundum*.

About 100 yards from the highway, the forest was less dense and trees were shorter. A rich stand of *Den. formosum* was found, with some plants within easy reach from the ground. *Den. secundum* was also growing among *Den. formosum*. In more shaded areas, fairly low on tree trunks, were numerous hanging clumps of *Aer. odorata* clinging to the trees by a few roots, with the majority of roots dangling in the air. A plant of *Den. farmeri* was observed, indicating that this species is native to this area as well as the Chandhaburi region.

The next day we set out for Lang Suan, 46 miles from Chumporn. The durian season in Bangkok area had passed, but the season was just beginning here.

Mangosteen and rambutan were also just appearing, whereas in Chandhaburi the season was about over. The late fruiting season is an advantage. With its favorable climate, this area should develop into an important fruit growing region of Thailand.

We spent the night at Prachuab. The next morning, after stopping at the 302-kilometer post in Prachuab to observe and collect orchid, we returned to Bangkok.

ORCHID SPECIES OF NORTHEAST THAILAND, 1965

In the spring of 1965, we participated in another well-organized survey trip — this time to northeastern Thailand. This expedition was led by Dean Thiem Komkris of the Forestry Faculty of Kasetsart University and included J. D. Sinclair and Sanga Sabhasri of the Faculty of Forestry, and H. Kamemoto, Rapee Sagarik, Sangtham Komkris and Pravin Punsri of the Horticulture Department.

We left Bangkok in two Land Rovers on the morning of March 25 and took the Paholyothin Highway to Saraburi. Instead of going directly to the northeast via the Friendship Highway, we continued north through Lopburi to Nakornsawan where we stopped for lunch. We then drove on to Tak, a province in northwestern Thailand bordering Burma.

The next morning we visited the rehabilitation center for the hill tribe at Doi Mooser, about 2700 feet above sea level. The officers stationed here, many of whom were graduates of Kasetsart University, were trying to help the hill tribe people in gainful agricultural activities other than growing poppy, and were encouraging "permanent" farming instead of the "slash, burn and shift" cultivation which is so destructive to natural vegetation, including native orchid species.

On our return journey to Tak, we stopped at Lansang Forest Experiment Station. Attached to trees in the resthouse area were many orchid species collected from the surrounding area. Some of the readily recognized species were *Aerides crassifolia, Aer. falcata, Dendrobium chrysotoxum, Den. parishii, Den. pulchellum, Den. thyrsiflorum, Vanda coerulea* and *Vandopsis parishii*. The next day we visited Bhumipol, or Yanhee Dam, which was recently completed. We toured the facilities and took a boat trip on the large manmade lake. After lunch we drove on to Sukothai. About 20 miles from Tak, in Lanhoy, we saw a short, fleshy leaved *Rhynchostylis gigantea* var. *illustre* hanging on a large tree which had shed its leaves, thus exposing the orchid to the sun. After stopping briefly for a trek into the forest, we moved on and reached Pitsanuloke at 8 p.m.

The next morning, our group paid homage to Prabuddhajinaraj, one of the highly worshipped images of Buddha. We then took Friendship Highway No. 2, connecting Pitsanuloke with Amphur Lomsak in Petchaboon Province. A few miles off the highway, close to the office of Sakunothayan Sanctuary, was a tree loaded with *Ascocentrum miniatum*, with its bright yellow-orange flowers. In the nursery of the Sanctuary were kept such representative indigenous species of the area as *Aer. crassifolia, Aer. falcata, Aer. multiflora, Den. draconis, Den. nobile, Den. pulchellum, Grammatophyllum speciosum* and others.

We moved on to Tung Sanlangluang Sanctuary, where we were to spend the night. We drove into the forest, a mile from the headquarters, and came across a rich stand of the epiphytic *Cymbidium simulans*. A huge clump consisted of several hundred pseudobulbs with many pendulant inflorescences bearing at least 25 flowers each. We came to a densely forested area with relatively few botanicals. When we moved into a less dense area, we saw, high up on trees, beautiful displays of lavender flowers on long, hanging pseudobulbs. These belonged to the species *Den. lituiflorum*. In an area where deciduous trees and shrubs prevailed, we saw *Den. nobile*. On a tree on the bank of a stream was a large clump of *Den. dixanthum*, with its brilliant-yellow, delicately textured flowers. Penetrating still deeper, we came to a mixed evergreen forest at 2500 feet elevation. High up on trees, where a greater amount of sunlight was available, plants of *Den. dixanthum*, *Den. fimbriatum* and *Trichoglottis dawsoniana* were observed.

We left the Sanctuary at dawn the next morning. On the well-paved highway, we reached Amphur Lomsak in Petchaboon Province in half an hour. The road to Loei was in poor condition -- dusty, bumpy and very narrow in places. *Aer. falcata* came into view frequently as we drove by, indicating its common occurrence. About 40 miles from Lomsak, we spotted a flowering plant of *Den. chrysotoxum* on a tall tree, so we stopped to explore this area. We found *Aer. crassifolia*, *Den. draconis*, *Den. lituiflorum*, *Den. pulchellum*, *Den. secundum*, *Eria* sp. and *Bulbophyllum* sp.

As we drove on, we came to a small village at 2600 feet elevation, where refreshing cold drinks were most welcome after the hot and dusty drive. Loei was still about 50 miles away, so we pushed on. The road was beginning to run slightly downhill. We saw a heavy stand of *Asctm. miniatum* in full bloom, as well as species observed earlier. Another hour of driving brought us to a fork in the road, one leading to Dansai, the other to Loei. By this time we were completely covered with a thick layer of dust, and were looking for a place where we could wash and have our lunch with some potable water. About 2 p.m. we reached the small village of Nong Boa, which only a few days before had been ransacked by bandits. Here we found bottled beverages to go with our packed lunch.

The dusty, bumpy road now took us up and down hills and across shallow streams. Late in the afternoon we were in the vicinity of Ban Nongsangnoi village. The open, deciduous forest suggested that orchid species might be prevalent here, and soon we came upon a rich stand of *Den. chrysotoxum* in peak bloom. Several plants of *Den. pierardii*, *Den. pulchellum* and *Vdps. parishii* were also in flower. Various stages of growth, from very young seedlings to large flowering plants, were observed for most of the species. *Den. aggregatum* and *Den. draconis* were also available in this location.

In Ban Nongsangnoi, the villagers sold orchid plants to tourists and other travelers and to traders from Bangkok who sell orchid species at the weekend market.

96

The inhabitants of this region practice shifting cultivation and, when they cut down trees, they collect orchids for sale. A big clump of *Den. chrysotoxum* was selling for only 2½ cents at the village. To the northeast of this village was a high mountain known as Khao Prasert, where *Vanda denisoniana* is found.

We reached Loei at 6 p.m. and were received by the Governor of Loei and the Regional Forestry Officer. Dinner and entertainment were provided for the expedition team.

After breakfast on March 30, we left Loei for Khonkaen. The kilometer signs were now decreasing in number. Between the 140 and 128 kilometer markers, we spotted *Asctm. miniatum* in flower in a deciduous forest. Between the 133 and 134 kilometer posts was a sign indicating a side road leading to Phu Kradeung, the flora of which has been well investigated. As we entered Khonkaen Province, we came to the Northeast Forest Research Station at an altitude of 1000 feet. In the forest were *Aer. crassifolia*, *Aer. falcata*, *Aer. flabellata*, *Den. aggregatum*, *Den. chrysotoxum* and *Den. pulchellum*. As we approached Khonkaen, we saw *Rhy. gigantea* and *Rhy. coelestis* hanging high up on trees by a few roots, along with *V. lilacina*. We arrived in Khonkaen for lunch, then were taken on a tour of the new Khonkaen University which was still under construction. Enroute to Udornthani, we visited the site of Ubolratana Dam.

We spent the night at Udornthani and then proceeded to Nongkai, a city on the bank of the Khon River which separates Thailand and Laos. One of our Land Rovers broke down and it took until 3 p.m. to have it repaired. We were scheduled to reach Sakornnakorn via Udornthani. This route was well known for its many terrorist activities, so we drove at very high speeds to reach our destination before darkness fell. We spent the night at the resthouse of the Fisheries Station at Nongharn.

After breakfast we began the long journey ahead. The road to Kalasin was thickly covered with dust. When we entered the Phupan Sanctuary we began to see many orchids. We stopped our car and found a heavy concentration of orchid species. *Aer. crassifolia* and *Aer. multiflora* were most plentiful. Other species encountered in numbers were *Aer. falcata* var. *houlletiana*, the tetraploid form of *Aer. odorata*, *Den. delacourii*, *Den. secundum*, *Phal. cornu-cervi*, *V. brunnea*, *V. lilacina* and *Vdps. parishii*. This location was about 800 feet elevation with an annual rainfall of about 60 inches. We surveyed this area for about an hour and moved on, arriving in Kalasin about noon. We drove on to Khonkaen, where we spent the night, and returned to Bangkok the following day.

BANGKOK'S FABULOUS WEEKEND MARKET

For those not fortunate enough to have seen orchids in their native habitats in Thailand, a foray to the weekend market in Bangkok offers an excellent substitute. On nearly every weekend, the huge open space known as Sanam Luang, formerly the Royal Crematorium Ground, is converted into a market. Beginning Friday night, tents and other temporary shelters are installed, and by Saturday morning the open ground is transformed into a bustling marketplace. Almost everything is sold here from food items, plants, live birds, and pedigreed dogs to toys and balloons. It appears that the entire population of Bangkok gathers here to buy or sell goods. By Monday morning the stalls and goods are completely removed.

The plants are concentrated on both sides of the klong (canal). In the past, plants were transported to the marketplace via the klongs, but vehicular transport predominates today. All types of horticultural crops, including roses, bougainvilleas, hibiscus, foliage plants and orchids, are displayed by numerous vendors, A visit to this weekend market is a must for a tourist in Thailand interested in horticulture of the country.

From 1962 to 1965, we visited the weekend market with regularity to observe the year-round parade of orchid species assembled from their native habitats. At least six vendors displayed native orchid species. In greatest demand were attractive species of horticultural value. Those in bud or already in bloom commanded better prices than those without any signs of floral development. Consequently, species were generally collected during their flowering season. By visiting the weekend market regularly, you can obtain valuable information of the availability of species in Thailand, the relative abundance, the seasons of flowering, the popularity among growers, etc. Many botanicals also are available, and a fine collection of orchid species in Thailand can be developed without participating in an expedition to their native haunts. It might be well to arrive at the market early on Saturday before the rare or uncommon species are sold.

The number of vendors of native species and the quantity of plants offered for sale has not diminished over the years. During a visit to the weekend market in March 1973, most of the orchid species discussed in preceding chapters were on display, including the genera *Aerides*, *Ascocentrum*, *Dendrobium* (sections *Callista*, *Eugenanthe* and *Nigrohirsutae*), *Rhynchostylis*, *Trichoglottis*, *Vanda* and *Vandopsis*. A few *Paphiopedilum* species also were available. It is indeed surprising to see so many native orchid species collected from the wilds and offered for sale weekly with no signs of depletion of the native stands. Sooner or later, however, the rich resources are bound to dwindle.

98

APPENDIX A. CHROMOSOME NUMBERS OF THAI ORCHID SPECIES

Species	Chromosome Number (2n)
Aerides :	
Aer. crassifolia	38
Aer. falcata	38
Aer. falcata var. *houlletiana*	38
Aer. flabellata	38
Aer. mitrata	38
Aer. odorata	38, 76
Ascocentrum :	
Asctm. ampullaceum	38
Asctm. curvifolium	38
Asctm. miniatum	38
Calanthe :	
Cal. rubens	44
Cymbidium :	
Cym. ensifolium	40
Cym. finlaysonianum	40
Cym. insigne	40
Cym. lowianum	40
Cym. tracyanum	40
Dendrobium :	
Den. aggregatum	38
Den. arachnites	38
Den. capillipes	38
Den. cariniferum	38
Den. chrysanthum	38
Den. chrysotoxum	38
Den. crassinode	38
Den. crepidatum	38

99

Species	Chromosome Number (2n)

Dendrobium Continued :

Den. crystallinum	38
Den. cruentum	40
Den. delacourii	38
Den. densiflorum	40
Den. dixanthum	40
Den. draconis	38
Den. falconeri	38
Den. farmeri	40
Den. farmeri var. *aureoflava*	40
Den. fimbriatum	38
Den. fimbriatum var. *oculatum*	38
Den. findlayanum	38
Den. formosum var. *giganteum*	38
Den. friedericksianum	38
Den. hercoglossum	38
Den. heterocarpum	38
Den. infundibulum	38
Den. lituiflorum	38
Den. moschatum	38
Den. moschatum var. *cupreum*	38
Den. nobile	38
Den. parishii	38
Den. pierardii	38
Den. primulinum	38
Den. pulchellum	40
Den. scabrilingue	38
Den. secundum	40
Den. senile	38
Den. sutepense	38
Den. thyrsiflorum	40
Den. tortile	38
Den. trigonopus	38

Doritis :

Dor. pulcherrima	38
Dor. pulcherrima var. *buyssoniana*	76

Species	Chromosome Number (2n)
Gastrochilus :	
Gastr. calceolaris	38
Gastr. dasypogon	38
Grammatophyllum :	
Gram. speciosum	40
Paphiopedilum :	
Paph. barbatum	38
Paph. bellatulum	26
Paph. callosum	32
Paph. concolor	26
Paph. exul	26
Paph. godefroyae	26
Paph. niveum	26
Paph. parishii	26
Paph. sukhakulii	40
Paph. villosum	26
Phalaenopsis :	
Phal. cornu-cervi	38
Phal. decumbens	38
Renanthera :	
Ren. coccinea	38
Ren. histrionica	38
Ren. isosepala	38
Rhynchostylis :	
Rhy. coelestis	38
Rhy. gigantea	38
Rhy. gigantea var. *illustre*	38
Rhy. retusa	38
Spathoglottis :	
Spa. plicata	40

Species	Chromosome Number (2n)
Trichoglottis :	
Trgl. fasciata	38
Vanda :	
V. amesiana	38
V. brunnea	38
V. coerulea	38
V. coerulescens	38
V. denisoniana (brown)	38, 76
V. denisoniana (green to yellow)	38
V. hookeriana	38
V. lilacina	38
V. teres	38
Vandopsis :	
Vdps. gigantea	38
Vdps. lissochiloides	38
Vdps. parishii	38

SELECTED BIBLIOGRAPHY

Cumberledge, P. F., and V. M. S. Cumberledge. 1963. A preliminary list of the orchids of Khao Yai National Park. Nat. Hist. Bul. Siam Soc. 20 : 3.

Gagnepain, F., and A. Guillaumin. 1932-34. Orchidacees. *In* Flore Generale de L'Indo-Chine. Vol. 6, Series 2-5, p. 142-647.

Grant, B. 1895. The orchids of Burma. Rangoon.

Handbook Committee. 1969. Handbook on orchid nomenclature and registration. International Orchid Commission. Cambridge, Mass.

Hawkes, A. 1965. Encyclopaedia of cultivated orchids. Faber and Faber, Ltd., London.

Holttum, R. E. 1963. *Saccolabium* and *Rhynchostylis*. Amer. Orchid Soc. Bul. 32 : 26-28.

Holttum, R. E. 1963. Species names in the genus *Doritis*. The Orchid Rev. 71 : 154-156.

Holttum, R. E. 1964 (third ed). Flora of Malaya, Vol. I, Orchids. Government Printing Office. Singapore.

Holttum, R. E. 1965. Cultivated species of the orchid genus *Doritis* Lindl. Kew Bul. 19 : 207-212.

Hooker, J. D. 1895. A century of Indian orchids. Ann. Roy. Bot. Gar., Calcutta.

Kamemoto, H. 1963. Chromosomes and species relationships in the *Vanda* alliance. Proc. Fourth World Orchid Conf. p. 107-117.

Kamemoto, H. 1966. Cytogenetics of Asiatic orchids. Proc. Fifth World Orchid Conf. p. 133-136.

Kamemoto, H., and R. Sagarik. 1967. Chromosome numbers of *Dendrobium* species of Thailand. Amer. Orchid Soc. Bul. 36 : 889-894.

Kamemoto, H., R. Sagarik and S. Dieutrakul. 1963. Karyotype analysis of *Paphiopedilum* species of Thailand. The Kasetsart Jour. 3 : 69-78.

Kamemoto, H., R. Sagarik and S. Kasemsap. 1964. Chromosome numbers of sarcanthine orchid species of Thailand. Nat. Hist. Bul. Siam Soc. 20 : 235-241.

King, G., and R. Pantling. 1898. The orchids of Sikkim-Himalaya. Ann. Roy. Bot. Gar., Calcutta.

Royal Horticultural Society. 1972. Sander's list of orchid hybrids, addendum 1961-1970. Whitefriars Press Ltd., London.

Sagarik, R. 1961. "Chang-Daeng," famous variety of *Rhynchostylis gigantea*. Amer. Orchid Soc. Bul. 30 : 945-947.

Sagarik, R, 1963. Dendrobium growing in Thailand. Proc. Fourth World Orchid Conf. p. 230-235.

Sagarik R. 1966. Orchid collecting trips in Thailand. Proc. Fifth World Orchid Conf. p. 115-118.

Sagarik, R. 1971. The horticultural vandaceous orchid species of Thailand. Proc. Sixth World Orchid Conf. p. 161-163.

Sander, D. F., F. K. Sander and L. L. Sander. 1927. Sanders' orchid guide. St. Albens, England.

Sander, D. F., and W. J. Wreford. 1961. Sander's one-table list of orchid hybrids. 2 vols. David Sander's Orchids Ltd., England.

Sander. F. K. 1946. Sanders' complete list of orchid hybrids. Gibbs and Bamforth, Ltd., England.

Schlechter, R. 1927. Die Orchideen. Paul Parey, Berlin.

Schoser, G., and K. Senghas. 1965. *Paphiopedilum sukhakulii*, ein unerwarteter Fund aus Thailand. Die Orchidee 16.

Seidenfaden, G. 1970. Contributions to the orchid flora of Thailand, II. Bot. Tidsskr. 65 : 313-370.

Seidenfaden, G. 1972. Contributions to the orchid flora of Thailand, IV. Bot. Tidsskr. 67 : 76-127.

Seidenfaden, G., and T. Smitinand. 1959-1965. The orchids of Thailand. The Siam Soc., Thailand.

Seidenfaden, G., and T. Smitinand. 1970. Report of the Sixth Thai Danish Expedition, 1968. Nat. Hist. Bul. Siam Soc. 23 : 527-538.

Shindo, K., and H. Kamemoto. 1963. Chromosome numbers and genome relationships of some species in the *Nigrohirsutae* section of *Dendrobium*. Cytologia 28 : 68-75.

Smith, J. J. 1905. Die Orchideen von Java. Flora Buitenzorg 6. Leiden.

Tanaka, R., and H. Kamemoto. 1972. A tabulation of chromosome numbers in Orchidaceae. *In* The Orchids, Culture and Breeding. Japan Orchid Soc., p. 667-773.

Williams, B. S. 1894. The orchid grower's manual. Germany.

Withner, C. L. 1959. The orchids - - a scientific survey. Ronald Press, New York.

104

PICTORIAL ILLUSTRATIONS

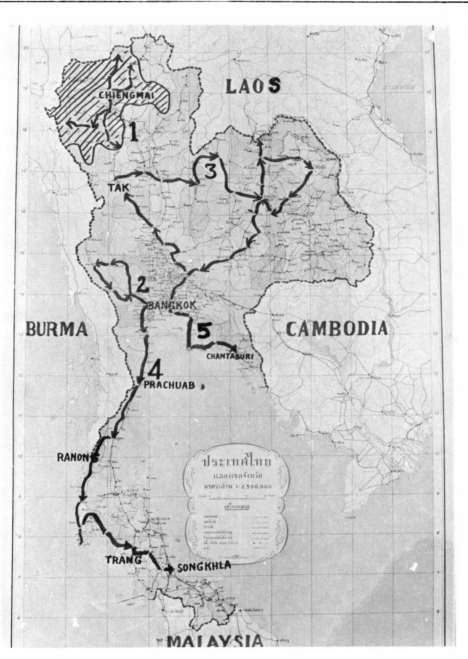

Major orchid collecting routes : 1–Chiengmai region in northern Thailand; 2–Khanburi in western Thailand; 3–northwestern and northeastern Thailand; 4–southwestern and peninsular Thailand; 5–Chandhaburi in southeastern Thailand.

COLLECTING ORCHIDS IN KHAOKHIEO

Collecting orchids from a felled tree.

Sorting the collected orchids.

COLLECTING ORCHIDS IN KHANBURI

Rapee Sagarik gathering
Trichoglottis fasciata.

Ignoring the clumps
of *Coelogyne* sp. for
Vandopsis parishii.

Photographing
Vandopsis parishii.

COLLECTING ORCHIDS IN KHANBURI

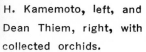

H. Kamemoto, left, and Dean Thiem, right, with collected orchids.

Down the River Kwai.

Returning by railway scooter.

CHIENGMAI ORCHIDS

Dendrobium draconis

Dendrobium secundum

Cymbidium finlaysonianum on
Palmyra palms at Petchburi.

Cymbidium finlaysonianum
at Chumporn.

Dendrobium formosum var. *giganteum* at Ranong.

Doritis pulcherrima off 302-kilometer post.

Collecting *Trichoglottis fasciata*.

At 318—kilometer post.

113

Rhynchostylis coelestis and
Eulophia keithii near 318-
kilometer post.

Pineapple production.

Clearing land for
more pineapples.

WEEKEND MARKET

Transporting plants
by boats.

Mostly sarcanthine
Orchid species.

Rapee Sagarik
inspecting orchid species.

115

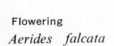

Flowering
Aerides falcata

Various orchid species.

Potted flowering
Dendrobium species.

116

Aerides   odorata
diploid   form   from   Southwest   Thailand

Aerides   odorata
tetraploid form
from   Northeast   Thailand

Aerides   odorata
tetraploid form
from   North Thailand

117

Aerides falcata   *Aerides falcata* **var.** *houlletiana*

Aerides multi flora

Aerides flabellata

119

Aerides crassifolia

Aerides mitrata

120

Arundina graminifolia

Ascocentrum curvifolium

Ascocentrum miniatum

Ascocentrum ampullaceum

123

Calanthe
vestita

Calanthe
rubens

Calanthe
cardioglossa

Coelogyne cumingii

Coelogyne virescens

Cymbidium lowianum

Cymbidium tracyanum

Cymbidium siamense

Cymbidium ensifolium

Cymbidium finlaysonianum.

Cymbidium simulans

Cymbidium simulans

Dendrobium aggregatum

Dendrobium chrysotoxum

129

Dendrobium farmeri

Dendrobium thyrsiflorum

Dendrobium densiflorum

Dendrobium farmeri var. aureoflava

Dendrobium aphrodite

Dendrobium chrysanthum

Dendrobium crepidatum

Dendrobium capillipes

Dendrobium crassinode

Dendrobium crystallinum

Dendrobium devonianum

Dendrobium dixanthum

Dendrobium falconeri

*Dendrobium
findlayanum*

*Dendrobium
friedericksianum*

*Dendrobium
friedericksianum*

Dendrobium fimbriatum   *Dendrobium fimbriatum* var. *oculatum*

Dendrobium hercoglossum

Dendrobium heterocarpum

Dendrobium moschatum

Dendrobium lituiflorum

Dendrobium pierardii

Dendrobium primulinum

Dendrobium wardianum

139

Dendrobium parishii

Dendrobium pulchellum

Dendrobium nobile

Dendrobium senile

Dendrobium tortile

Dendrobium formosum var. *giganteum.*

Dendrobium infundibulum

Dendrobium sutepense

Dendrobium scabrilingue

Dendrobium draconis

Dendrobium cariniferum

Dendrobium bellatulum

Dendrobium margaritaceum

Dendrobium trigonopus

Dendrobium cruentum

Dendrobium delacourii

Dendrobium secundum

Doritis pulcherrima
from peninsular Thailand

Doritis pulcherrima
from eastern Thailand

Doritis pulcherrima
var. *buyssoniana*

Doritis pulcherrima   left
var. *buyssoniana*   right

Gastrochilus dasypogon

Gastrochilus bellinus

Grammatophyllum speciosum

Habenaria rhodocheila

Habenaria columbae

Habenaria medioflexa

Paphiopedilum bellatulum

Paphiopedilum concolor

153

*Paphiopedilum
niveum*

*Paphiopedilum
niveum* "Ang Thong,"

*Paphiopedilum
godefroyae*

*Paphiopedilum
parishii*

*Paphiopedilum
exul*

*Paphiopedilum
villosum*

155

Paphiopedilum callosum.

Paphiopedilum barbatum

Paphiodedilum sukhakulii

Phaius tankervilliae

Phalaenopsis cornu-cervi

Phalaenopsis decumbens

Renanthera coccinea

Renanthera isosepala

159

Rhynchostylis   gigantea   typical   form

Rhynchostylis   gigantea   alba

Rhynchostylis gigantea amethyst — purple

Rhynchostylis   retusa   typical form

Rhynchostylis retusa alba

Rhynchostylis coelestis typical form *Rhynchostylis coelestis* alba

Spathoglottis plicata

Spathoglottis lobbii

Trichoglottis fasciata

Trichoglottis dawsoniana

*Vanda
teres*

*Vanda
hookeriana*

*Vanda
amesiana*

Vanda coerulea tessellated.

Vanda coerulea pink.

Vanda coerulea not tessellated.

Color variation in *Vanda denisoniana*

Vanda coerulescens

Vanda lilacina

Vanda parviflora

Vanda brunnea

Vanda besoni

Vandopsis   lissochiloides

Vandopsis   gigantea

Vandopsis parishii

Vandopsis parishii var. *marriottiana*

INDEX

INDEX

178

184